Contents for Diagramming Worktext

Worktext Answers are placed after page 72. The answer pages are numbered with lower case Roman numerals, while the text pages they refer to are given at the top of each page.

The purpose of diagramming is to help you think clearly. There is no point asking other people -- even God -- to express themselves clearly if you don't think clearly. For the Chinese, it was part of honoring the ancestors to learn their complicated writing. It really has a moral dimension.

I am the Lord, unrivaled,
I have not spoken in secret
in some corner of a darkened land.
I have not said to Jacob's descendants,
'Seek me in chaos.'
I, Yahweh, speak with directness
I express myself with clarity.
            Isaiah 45:19, The Jerusalem Bible

Introduction:

Usually, we teach diagramming very gradually spreading it over several years because of the numerous details. The trouble is, diagramming is a sort of language, though exclusively a written one, and until you can use it for everyday thinking, you can't become accustomed to it. There are many parts of English grammar that seem too complex to teach in one year, yet even little children use them -- and use them properly -- every day. So perhaps grammar could be taught earlier and faster if it were made simple and visual. I am happy to report that some people are now teaching diagrams in first grade, right when they teach that every sentence has a subject and a verb. That is chapter one of this book, and you can begin teaching this chapter the day you teach that every sentence has a subject and a verb.

Diagramming is actually about syntax, which is the way words are related in sentences, not about grammar, which is the proper construction of specific words within sentences. Of course the disciplines of grammar and syntax overlap because the proper construction of a word often depends upon the way it is used in a sentence; but there is a difference. Syntax is the essential; grammar is the surface.

In these pages, you will learn elementary diagramming in simple steps. Each chapter does have just a taste of material slightly more advanced than the chapter title. It is not so difficult to work out these teasers, and then if you think it over, you may find that you already know the next chapter. In the final chapter, I have offered a peek into the vast world of complex diagrams.

I hope you will enjoy diagramming because it is very beautiful.

The companion volume, <u>The First Whole Book of Diagrams</u> was originally intended to be a diagrammer's reader. You can learn a lot just by reading beautiful diagrams and puzzling them out. By having the image of a beautiful diagram in your mind, you will prepare yourself for each step along the way.

In this edition, I want to thank all my past students for their helpful suggestions, and especially my daughter Ruth Daly, for her patient editorial work and my husband for his proofing again and again.

Chapter I The Sentence, Subject and Verb

We communicate our thoughts, not just in words, but in sentences.

A sentence is a sequence of words
whose relationships express a unit of thought.

Putting the words in one order means one thing; putting them in another order usually means a different thing. If I say "Children play with dogs," it doesn't seem very different from saying "Dogs play with children." But if I say, "Children drink milk," that is not at all the same as saying, "Milk drinks children." That would be the beginning of a nightmare.

Sometimes, especially when we have a long sentence, it is hard to be sure just exactly how the words are related. If you become confused about the relationships between words, you no longer know what the sentence means.

It may be that the sentence was not well put together. Or it may be that you need to think a little harder about how the words fit. Diagramming is a way of mapping how the words in a sentence are related to each other and how the ideas in a sentence fit. When you can diagram a sentence, then you know exactly how the words are related, and if the sentence still doesn't make sense, then either you need a dictionary, or the person who made the sentence needs to fix it.

The first lesson about sentences is that since they express thoughts, and since thoughts are about things, there has to be a word which names the thing we are thinking about. This word is the subject. There must also be a part of the sentence which names what the subject does or what it is like. This part is called the predicate, and the main part of the predicate is the verb.

In this chapter, we will learn to diagram simple sentences that have only a subject and a verb. Each chapter will introduce more sentence parts.

Every sentence has a subject and a verb. The subject is a noun or a pronoun. It tells us who is doing something. The verb tells us what the subject is doing. Here is a sentence:

Snow falls.

Name the noun. _____

Name the verb. _____

The noun is snow. Snow is what the sentence is about. What does snow do? It falls. This is the verb.

Actually, in a longer sentence, it may be easier to find the verb first and the subject afterwards. Do it that way in this sentence:

The children of Holland race along its canals.

The verb is _____. Someone is doing this.

The noun is _____. This is who is doing it.

Now write a few sentences of your own. Make them short, but be sure each one has a subject and a verb.

_____

_____

_____

_____

_____

Here are a few sentences about things you might see in the grass. Find the subject and the verb in each sentence. You might underline the verb and circle the subject. One word is neither a noun nor a verb. Can you find it?

In the Grass

1 Wind whispers.
2 Sun shines.
3 Snakes slither.
4 Mice hide.
5 Crickets chirp.
6 Grasshoppers chew.
7 Beetles creep.
8 Ants march.
9 Clover grows.
10 The flowers open.
11 Butterflies stop.
12 Feet walk.

Now write your own story. Perhaps you could tell about some of the things you might see in a bush or from a bird's nest or from the ceiling of the room you are working in. Make short sentences, just things and what they do.

_____

_____

_____

_____

_____

_____

DIAGRAMS:

We have a special way of writing sentences to show the subject and the verb. It is called a diagram. The diagram helps us
to "see" syntax.

A diagram begins with a baseline where we write the
subject and the verb. Between them, another line cuts down
through the base line. It looks like this:

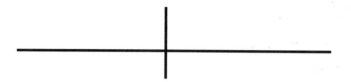

We place the subject before the vertical divider; the verb
goes after it. If we diagram the sentences from page three,
they look like this:

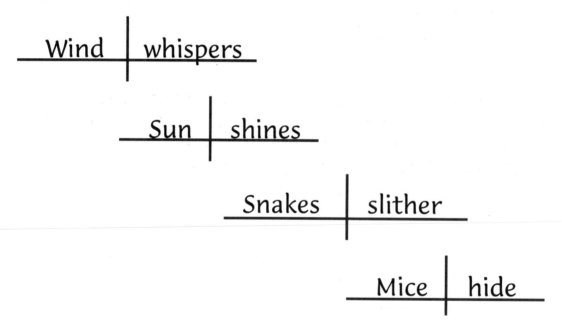

Remember, the subject is always a noun or a pronoun. The
verb is the action word. It tells us what the subject is doing.
Can you use the lines on the next page and finish the diagrams
from page 3? (One word is diagrammed for you. Look at it
and think about it. Is it a noun? Is it a verb? We will talk
about it in the next chapter.)

⁵ Crickets chirp.
⁶ Grasshoppers chew.
⁷ Beetles creep.
⁸ Ants march.

⁹ Clover grows.
¹⁰ The flowers open.
¹¹ Butterflies stop.
¹² Feet walk.

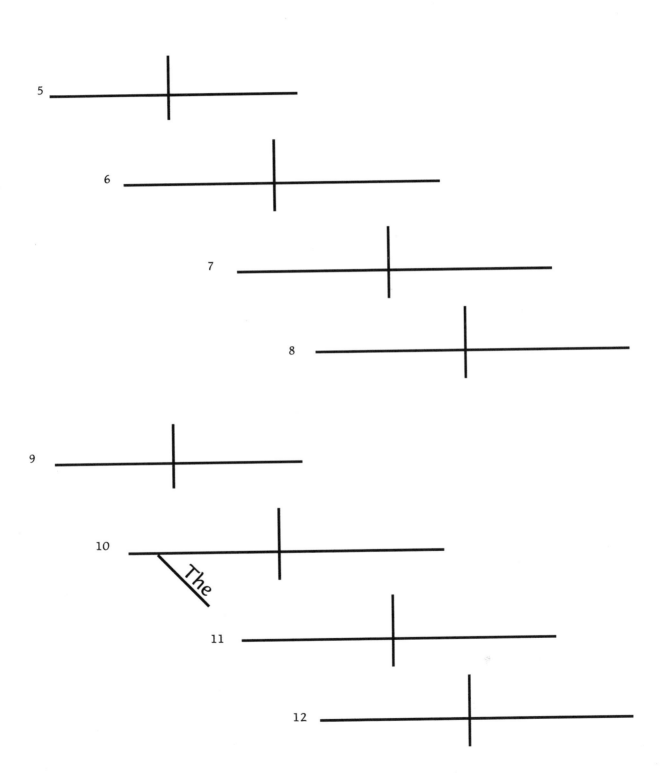

Now try writing and diagramming the subjects and verbs of your own sentences. You may use the ones you wrote before or write new ones. It is not always easy to make sentences with just two words, but it will help you to learn what subject and verb mean. "My house" is not a sentence. It is just one noun with a word that means it belongs to me. Since the house is not doing anything, it is not in a sentence. Of course a house never does do very much. But, "My house glows," is a sentence. The house where I grew up always had lights on in every room where we were reading; our neighbors called it "the hotel" because we had so many lights on.

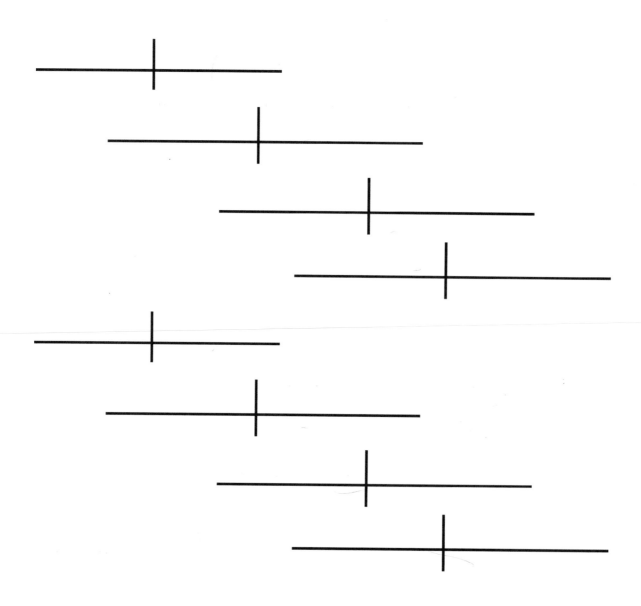

This page is for you to practice on. Ask someone to dictate short sentences to you, and write them on the lines you have. Pages from the first chapter of <u>The First Whole Book of Diagrams</u> will work well.

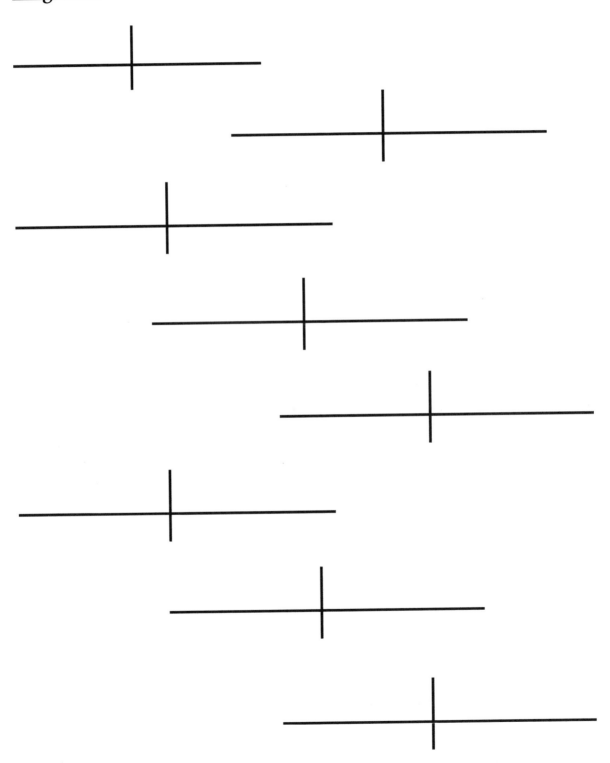

This page is also for practice. Write about some things that are beautiful, and diagram the subject and verb as you write. Keep it simple!

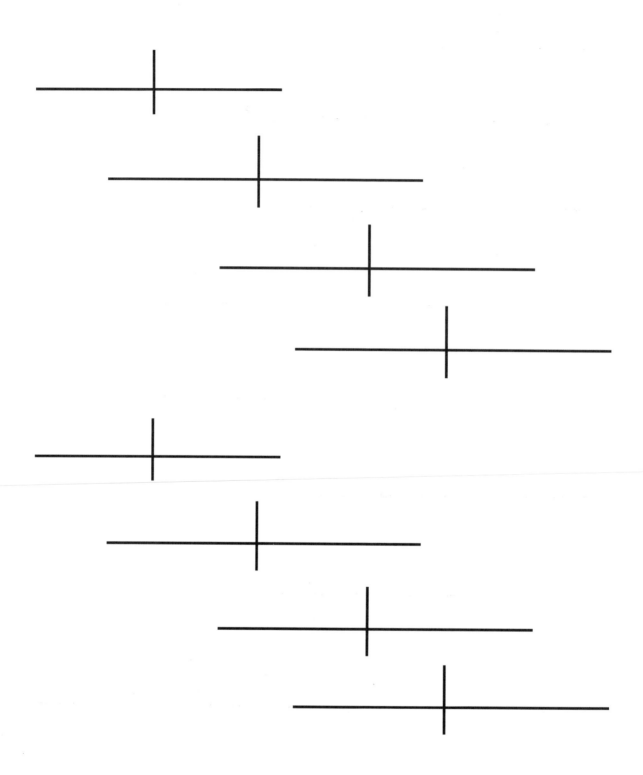

Chapter II Three Articles: The, An, A

Probably the most common word we say is "the." It's a word that goes with a lot of our nouns. We say:

the peach   the apple   the grapes

The word "the" is called an article. Now look at these sentences:

The peaches grow. The apples ripen. The grapes darken.

What are the subjects? _____ _____

_____

What are the verbs? _____ _____

_____

Now look at the diagrams:

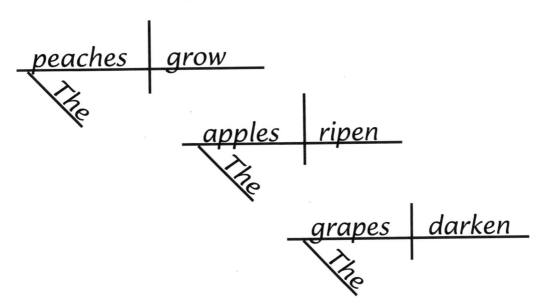

When we diagram sentences with the article "the", we write it on a slanted line, just below its noun. Try these sentences about the orchard. You will need to add lines for "the" in each sentence:___

The Orchard:

¹Spring comes.
²The trees bud.
³The blossoms open.
⁴The bees visit.

⁵The wind blows.
⁶The petals fall.
⁷The fruit grows.
⁸The children come.

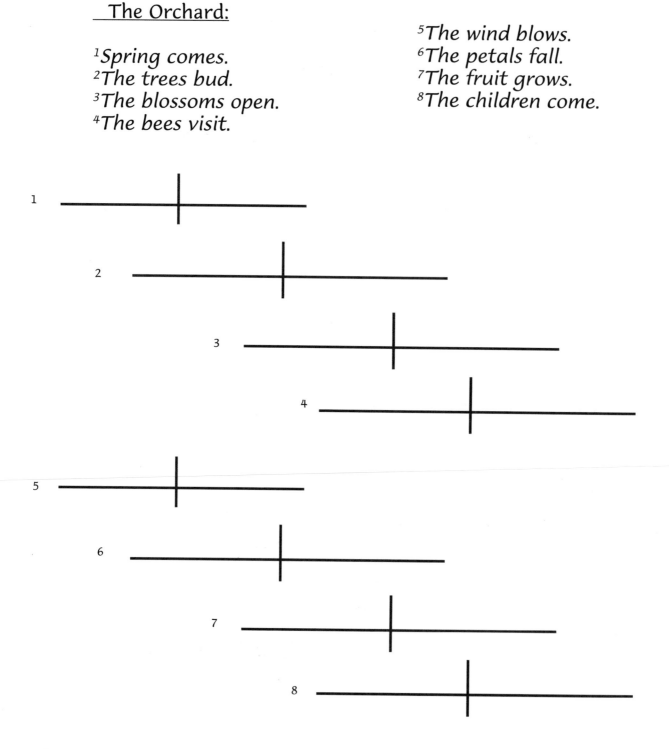

There are two more articles in English. The word "a" is an article. We say:

a peach, a melon, a banana

If a word begins with a vowel, we say "an" instead of "a". We say:

an apple , an orange, an olive

Both articles are diagrammed just like the word "the":

There are just three articles in English: <u>The, An, and A.</u>

<u>The</u> apple falls. <u>A</u> banana softens. <u>An</u> orange brightens.

When you diagram any article, you place it on a slanted line below the noun it refers to:

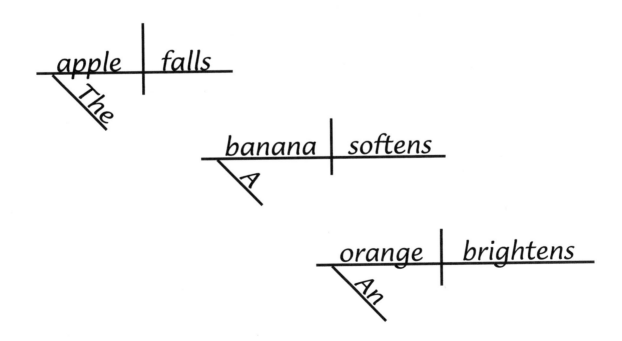

Diagrams:

We always diagram an article on a slanted line just below its noun. Here is a story about acorns. Can you diagram it? (The word "one" is not an article but it goes with "acorn". Can you see why it has been diagrammed the way it is? See the next chapter.)

The Acorn

[1] Springtime comes. [2] An oak grows. [3] The acorns ripen. [4] A wind roars. [5] The acorns fall.

[6] A squirrel comes. [7] He chatters. [8] He eats. [9] The acorns disappear.

[10] The leaves fall. [11] The acorns hide. [12] A snowstorm passes.

[13] Spring returns. [14] One acorn sprouts. [15] An oak grows.

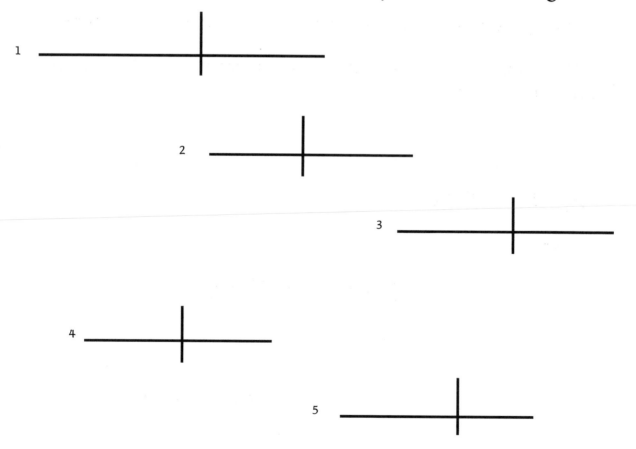

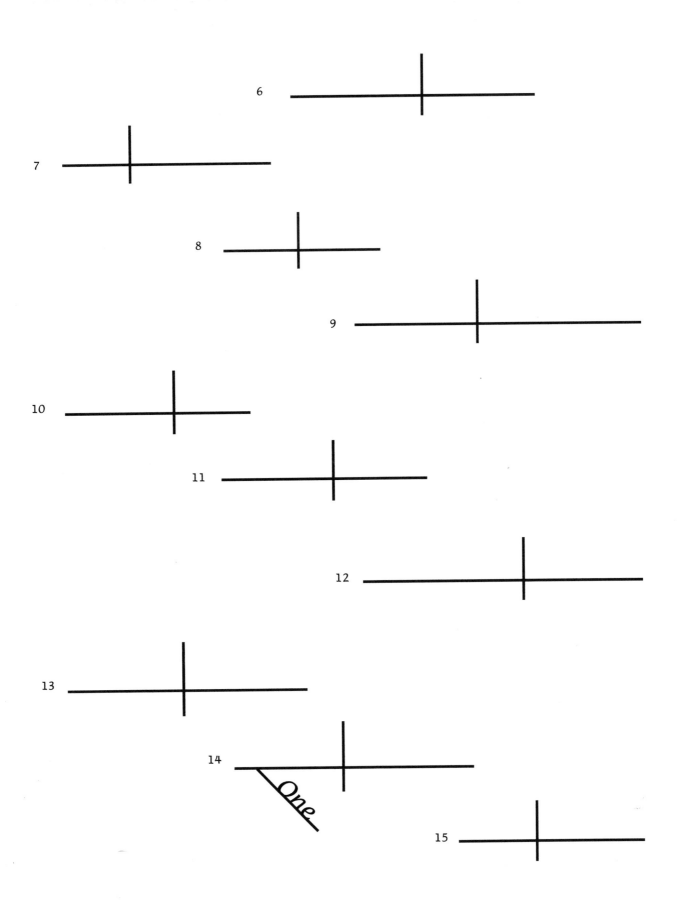

6

7

8

9

10

11

12

13

14 *One.*

15

Try diagramming this simple story. It tells how the mother eagle flies below her young to catch them when they are learning to fly. There are two extra words. Can you figure out where to put them?

The Fledgling

[1] An eaglet looks. [2] He hops. [3] The little wings flutter. [4] The fledgling tumbles.

[5] The mother comes. [6] A great wing appears. [7] The eaglet is caught.

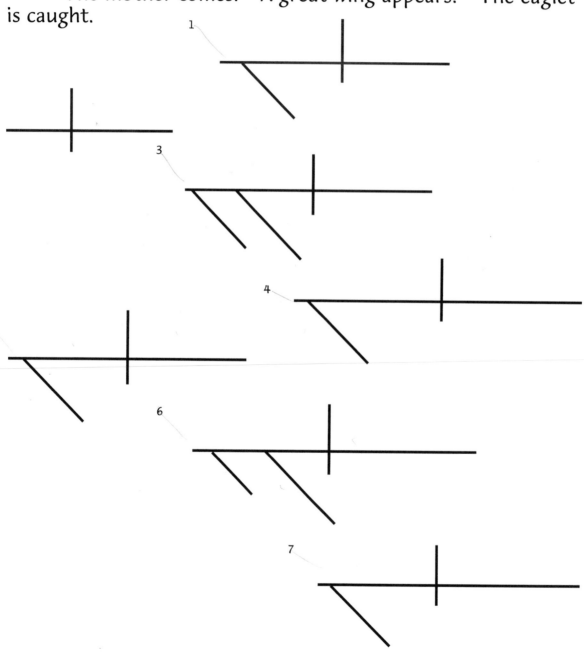

Now write your own story and diagram it as you go:

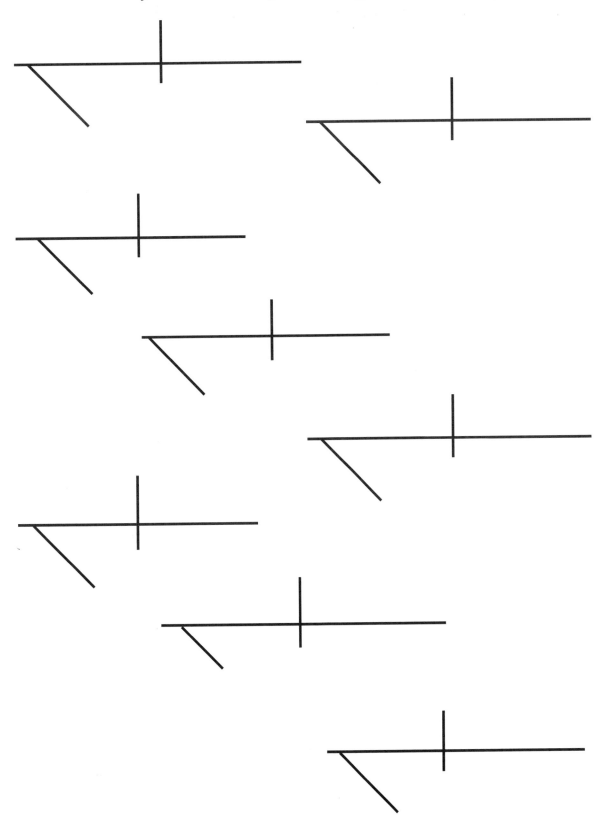

Write another story. Diagram the subject and verb of each
sentence. What other words can you put into the diagrams?

Chapter III Adjectives

Many of the words that make a sentence interesting are called adjectives. Adjectives are words that describe nouns. They make a picture more exact. Here is a very simple sentence with its diagram:

The sun shines.

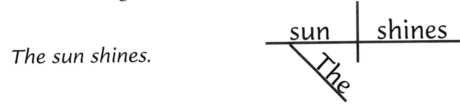

It has an article, a noun, and a verb. We know it is about the daytime, but that's all we know. Now look at two more sentences:

The hot sun shines.   The pallid sun shines.

"Hot" and "pallid" are adjectives. The word "hot" suggests a picture of the summer or the desert. The word "pallid" suggests a day in winter or in fog. These words tell us more about the sun. In a diagram, the adjectives go under their nouns, on a slanted line, just like articles. Here is how we diagram adjectives:

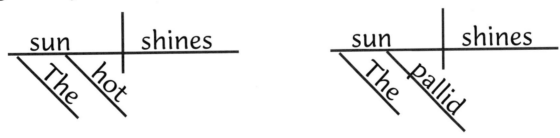

What adjectives would you use for the moon?

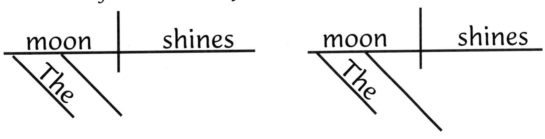

Now let's add articles and adjectives to some of the sentences we used on page 3. Can you still diagram them?

In the Grass II

[1]The gentle wind whispers.
[2]The golden sun shines.
[3]Little snakes slither.
[4]A quick mouse hides.

[5]The musical crickets chirp.
[6]The hungry grasshoppers chew.
[7]A shiny beetle creeps.
[8]The busy ants work.

[9]The rich clover grows.
[10]Little white flowers open.
[11]One blue butterfly stops.
[12]Bare feet walk.

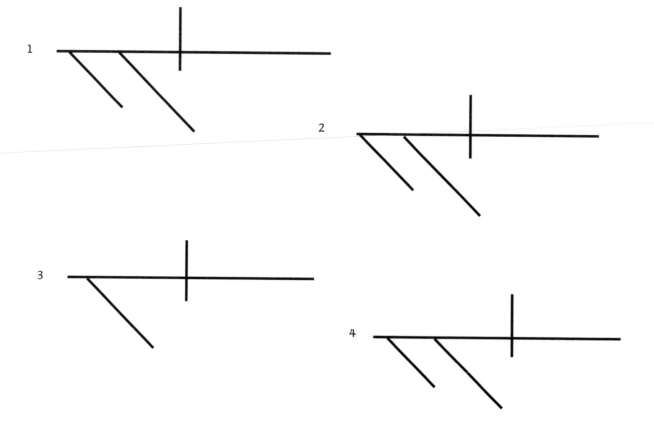

You know where
to make lines for the
articles and adjec-
tives; go ahead.

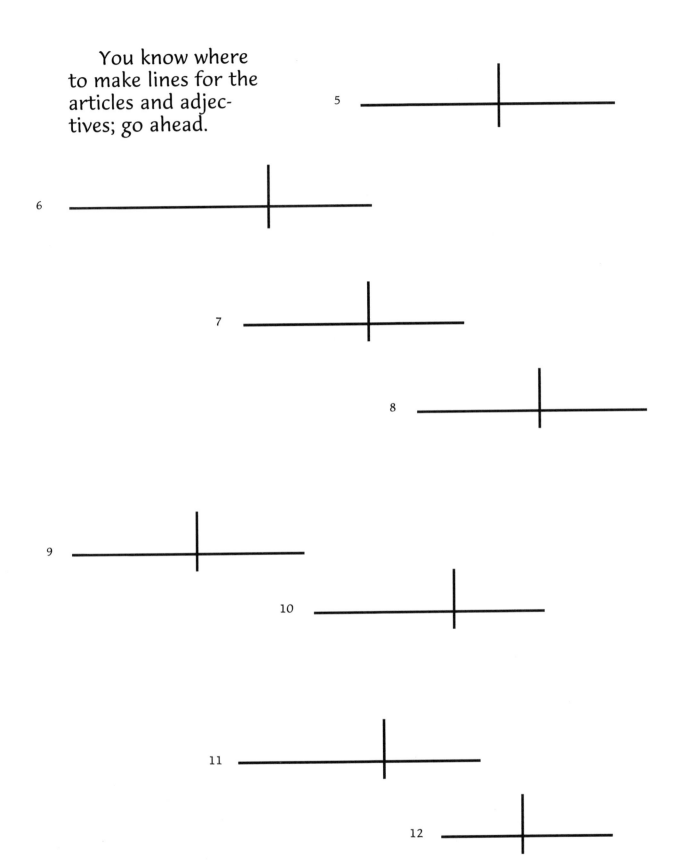

PRONOUNS AS ADJECTIVES:

Pronouns replace nouns. There are also adjectival pronouns, (called pronominal adjectives). For example, we can say:

Jane's hat   the boy's dog   the elephant's child

Or we might say:

my hat   your dog   her child

When we use pronouns as adjectives, they are just like adjectives. When we diagram them, they go right under the nouns they refer to. Look at these sentences with their diagrams:

Jane's hat tips.
My hat tips.

The boy's dog barks.
Your dog barks.

The elephant's child asks.
Her child asks.

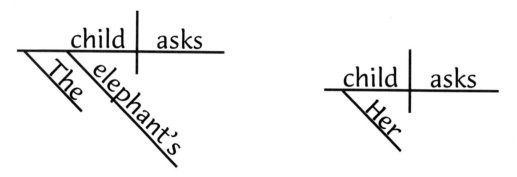

A NOTE ABOUT CONJUNCTIONS:

Sometimes two words have the same syntactical position in a sentence. You might have two subjects or two verbs; you might have two adjectives for the same noun. If they are connected by the word "and," we have to show that on the diagram too. Such sentences are very common, and no more difficult to diagram than to speak.

In the case of compound nouns or verbs, we simply take the line where they occur in the diagram and split it in two, with a little corner between and a dotted line for the word "and" or whatever conjunction is used.

We can have two subjects:

Jack and Jill went up the hill.

We can have two verbs:

The seasons come and go.

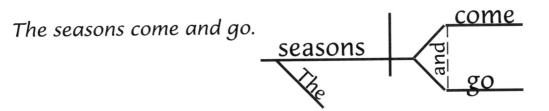

We can have two adjectives. In this case, we need only add the dotted line between the two words on their slanted lines:

The clever and beautiful fox prevails.

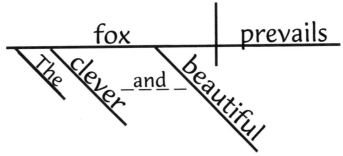

Here is a familiar story by Kipling, using adjectives and pro-nominal adjectives (pronoun adjectives, like "his" and hers). Can you diagram it on the lines provided? The word "and" is provided for a double subject and for a compound sentence. Does that make sense to you?

<u>The Elephant's Child</u>

[1]The elephants's child wonders. [2]He asks and asks.
[3]His tired mother scolds. [4]His grouchy father scowls.
[5]The tall ostrich kicks. [6]The hairy baboon chatters.
[7]The curious elephant travels. [8]His many questions con-tinue. [9]The crafty crocodile whispers. [10]The elephant listens, and the crocodile bites.
[11]The elephant's nose stretches!

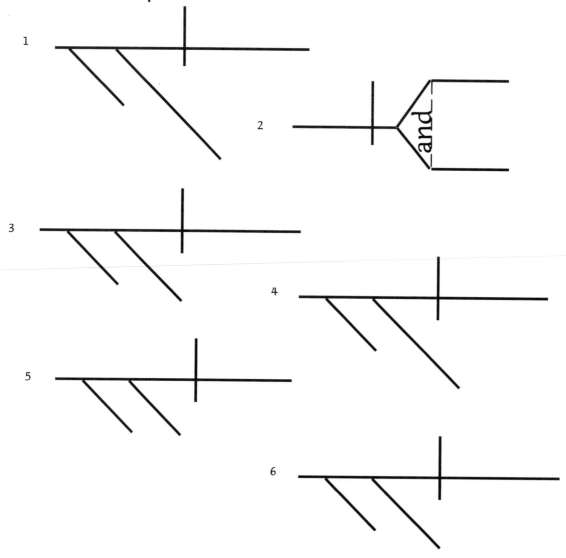

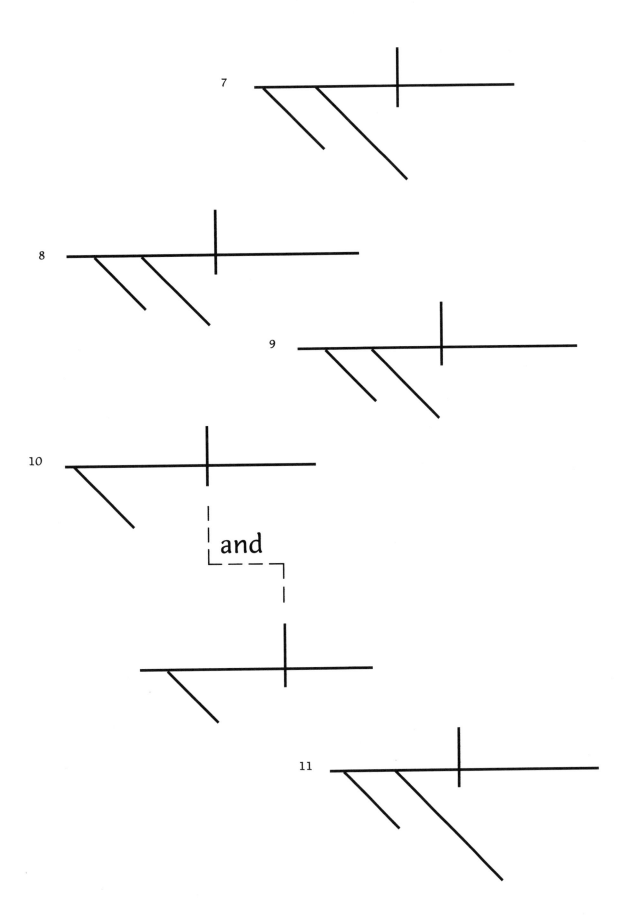

7

8

9

10

and

11

In general, we think of some words as nouns, others as verbs, still others as adjectives or something else. But really, it all depends on how the word is used in a sentence. Look at these words:

milk   desert   travel   red   tree

Do you think they are nouns, verbs, or adjectives?

Now look at the sentences below. Tell whether the underlined word is a noun, a verb, or an adjective.

1) Sarah drinks <u>milk</u>.
   Sarah can <u>milk</u> the cow.
   <u>Milk</u> soup with pepper is good for a sick child.
2) The <u>desert</u> is dry.
   The <u>desert</u> flowers are brilliant.
3) Ann enjoys <u>travel.</u>
   She will <u>travel</u> by plane.
   The <u>travel</u> agent will help.
4) The <u>red</u> light is the stoplight.
   <u>Red</u> means stop.
5) The <u>tree</u> is very tall.
   The <u>tree</u> trunk is rough.
   My dog can <u>tree</u> any cat in the neighborhood.

An adjective is a word that describes a noun. If you think a word is an adjective, find the noun it describes. In the sentences above, all the underlined words were used once as adjectives, but then as other parts of speech. It all depends on usage.

One way to check usage is to diagram, because a diagram is a map of usage. Look at the diagrams of the first three sets of sentences. After studying them, can you diagram the fourth and fifth sets on your own paper?

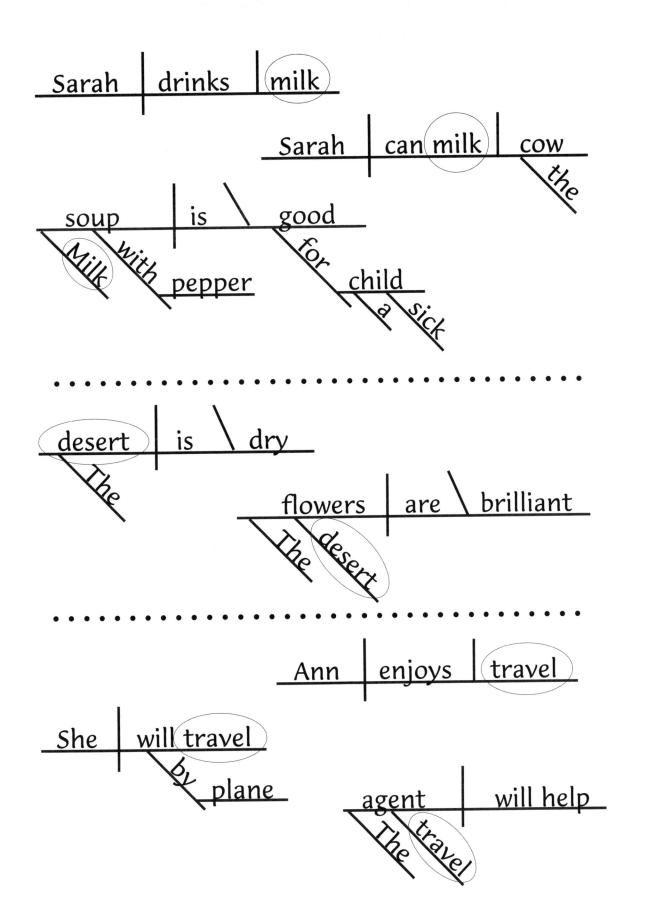

Your Turn

Perhaps you find my stories dull. It is difficult to write interesting sentences using only very simple grammar. You try it! Your everyday grammar is quite complex. If you cannot diagram the entire sentence, just find the subject and verb and some adjectives for the subject or have someone dictate to you from Chapter III of <u>The First Whole Book of Diagrams.</u>

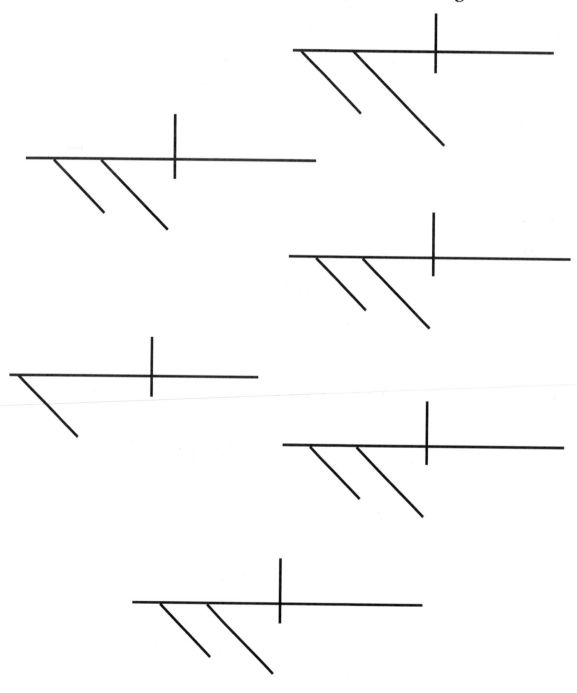

Chapter IV Direct Objects

Most often, subjects and verbs have direct objects. Direct objects are nouns or pronouns and the subject does something to them. They receive its action. Whenever we are looking for the direct object, we say "the subject... the verb... what?" For example, in the sentence:

Dogs chase cats

"Dogs" is the subject. "Chase" is the verb. To find the direct object, we say, "Dogs chase what?" "Cats" is the answer. "Cats" is the direct object in this sentence. You have already seen some diagrams of direct objects. They look like this:

$$\underline{\text{Dogs} \mid \text{chase} \mid \text{cats}}$$

Notice how the vertical line between the subject "dogs" and the verb "chase" goes though the baseline; but the vertical line between "chase" and "cats" does not. There is an important reason for this. But first, practice a few yourself. Try these sentences:

Peter's wife likes pumpkins.
The hazy skies make gentle colors.

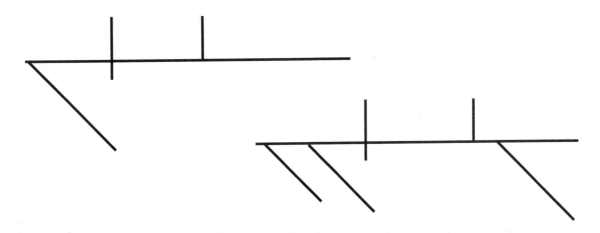

SUBJECT AND PREDICATE:

We have talked about the subject and the verb. We can also talk about the subject and the *predicate*, or about the *complete subject* and the *complete predicate*. The main part of the predicate is the verb; but the *complete predicate is (almost[1]) everything else in the sentence except the subject and its adjectives.* The subject is the person or thing that is doing something; and the complete subject includes *all the articles, adjectives, and other modifiers that go with the subject.*

So, in the sentence "Dogs chase cats, "dogs" is the complete subject, but the complete predicate is "chase cats." The verb is just "chase" but the complete predicate includes the direct object.

---

[1]If you call someone by name, or say "Wow!" or "Oh!" these words are neither part of the subject nor part of the predicate. They are called interjections. They are placed at the upper left of the diagram, on a line by themselves:

Alonzo, I have your jacket.
Oh! Your dog is chasing our cat.

When you diagram a sentence, the vertical line that cuts through the baseline of a diagram separates the complete subject from the complete predicate. *This is the most important line in the diagram.*

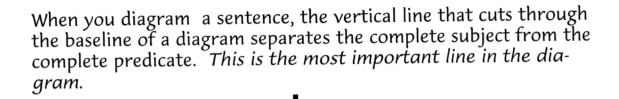

When you look at a diagram, you can see that the direct object is part of the complete predicate: the line that separates it from the verb does *not* cut through the baseline of the diagram. It looks like this:

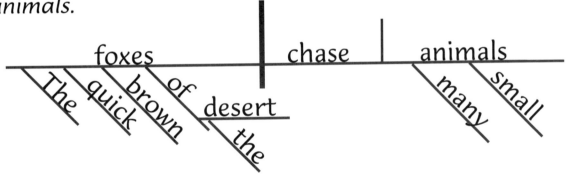

Here are two longer sentences to show you how it looks:

The quick brown foxes of the desert chase many small animals.

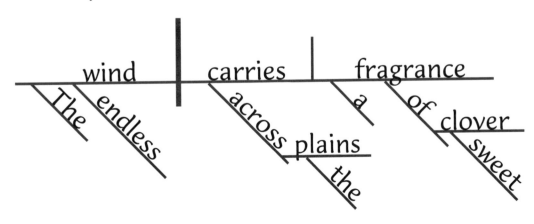

The endless wind carries a fragrance of sweet clover across the plains.

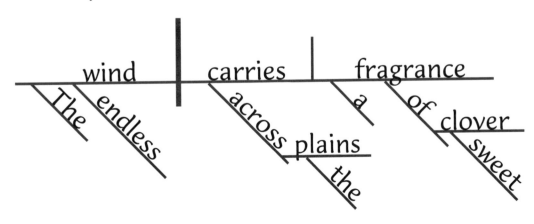

Analyze and diagram the following sentences, darkening the line between subject and predicate:

The naughty little rabbit ate all my lettuce.

The simple subject is _____.
The complete subject is _____
The verb, or simple predicate, is _____.
The direct object is _____. (Ask yourself, "Rabbit ate what?)
The complete predicate is _____.
   Here is the diagram:

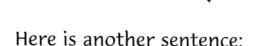

Here is another sentence:

The rugged old fishermen cast their great nets.

The simple subject is _____.
The complete subject is _____
The verb, or simple predicate, is _____.
The direct object is _____. (Ask, "Fishermen cast what?")
The complete predicate is _____.
   Here is the diagram:

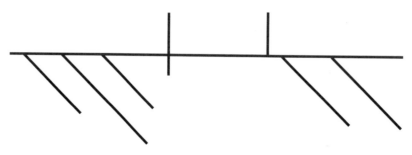

Try to work these out more independently:

The morning sun brightens the pale sandstone.

The simple subject is _____.
The complete subject is _____
The verb, or simple predicate, is _____.
The direct object is _____. (Ask: The sun brightens what?)
The complete predicate is _____.

Diagram it here, adding the lines you need:

Find subject, complete subject, verb, direct object, and complete predicate for this sentence:

A thousand spider webs carried the bright morning dew.

Diagram these sentences:
[1]The sturdy pine trees produce cones.
[2]The brown cones have little scales.
[3]These scales hide tiny seeds.
[4]The busy squirrels and little birds find the seeds.
[5]One small seed hides and sprouts.

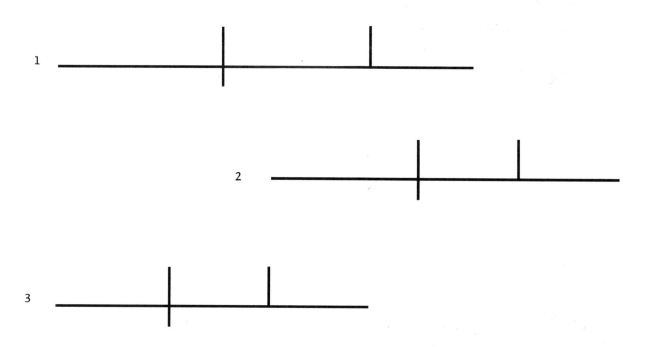

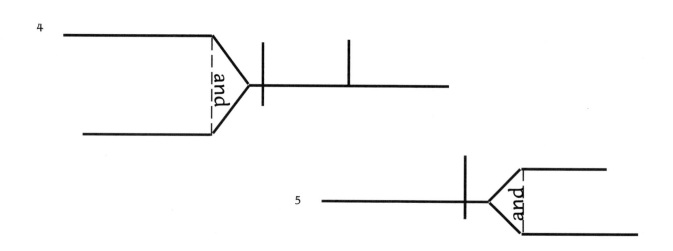

Have someone dictate sentences with direct objects. Keep them simple. The easiest way to compose a sentence with syntax that you can diagram is to take a sentence you know and compose one which has the same rhythm. Can you think of a sentence with two subjects?

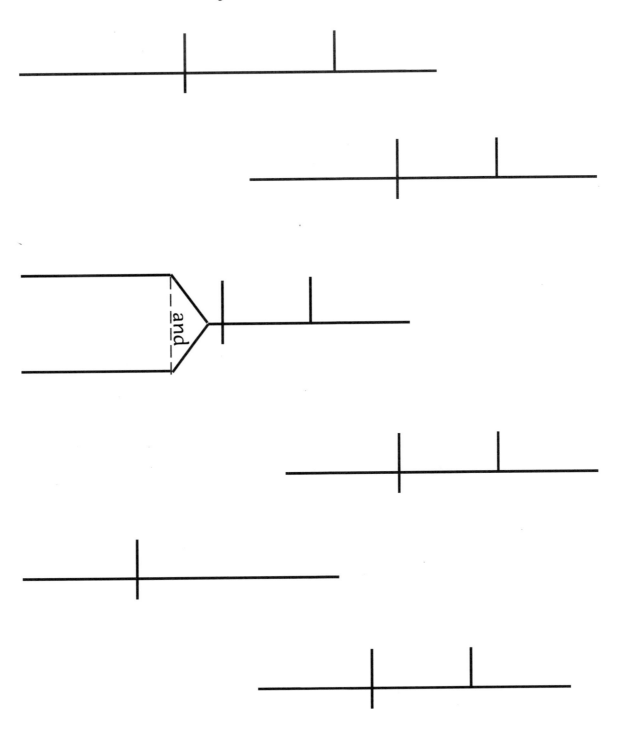

Finally, try diagramming sentences of your own composition. If you cannot diagram everything you write, at least diagram the subject, the verb, the direct object (if there is one), and all the adjectives. Can you compose a sentence with two verbs?

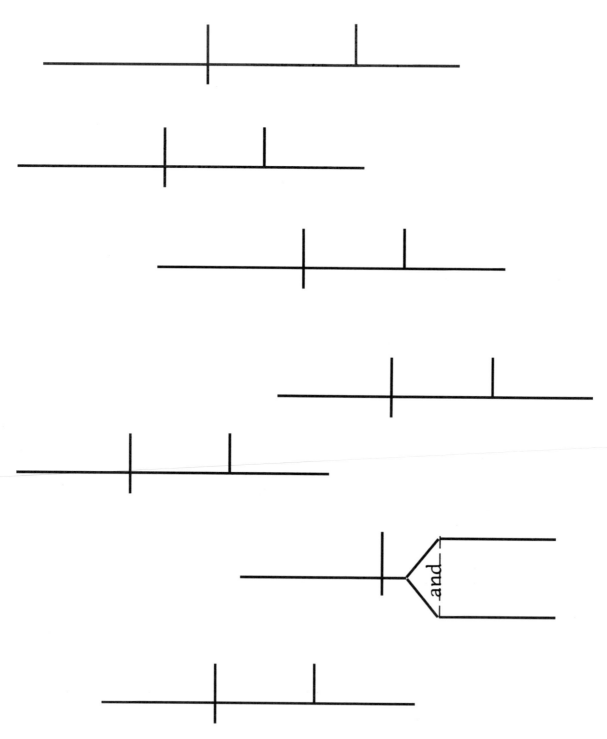

Chapter V Linking Verbs

THE VERB "TO BE":

Some verbs have no direct object. Instead, they link the subject to another name for itself, or to a description. The forms of the verb "to be" -- am, is, are, was, were, be, been -- never take direct objects. Look at this sentence:

The sky is blue.

The subject is "sky". The verb is "is". When we ask "the sky... is... what?", the answer is "blue". But the sky is not doing anything. And "blue" is not receiving any action from the sky. "Blue" is simply an adjective describing the sky. We diagram it this way:

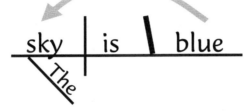

As you can see, we put the word blue in the position of the direct object, but we slant the dividing line so that it points towards the subject. (The arrows are not really part of the diagram.) This is how we show that our verb is a linking verb.

Here is another example:

The horse is an animal.

The subject is "horse." The verb is "is." When we ask, "The horse... is... what?", the answer is "an animal." But "animal" does not receive any action from the horse. It just tells us where the horse fits into the kingdom of life. Diagram it.

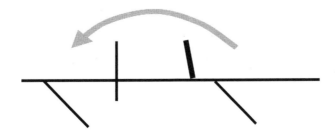

As I said, the arrow is not part of the diagram.

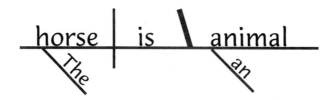

That is how it's done. Again, see how the vertical divider after the verb is tipped towards the subject? This shows that "animal" is not the direct object. It is a word that refers back to the subject.

There are several forms of the verb "to be" and the best thing is to memorize them at once. Sometimes these verbs are used as auxiliaries for the progressive forms of other verbs, like the "is" in "is going". Used alone, however, they are always linking verbs. They may also be called copulative verbs. Anyway, memorize them:

am, is, are, was, were, be, been

as well as:

will be, must be, shall be, should be, has been, had been, would have been, must have been, etc.

Now diagram these sentences, full of verbs of being. Notice how some end with nouns, some with adjectives. Circle the nouns and box the adjectives so that you notice which is which. We will be talking about them later. I have diagrammed those parts of the sentences that we have not yet discussed.

[1]Lions are beautiful creatures. [2]Their fur is golden. [3]Their manes are long. [4]Lions are not gentle. [5]Their paws are enormous. [6]The great roar of a lion is a terrible sound. [7]A hungry lion is fierce.

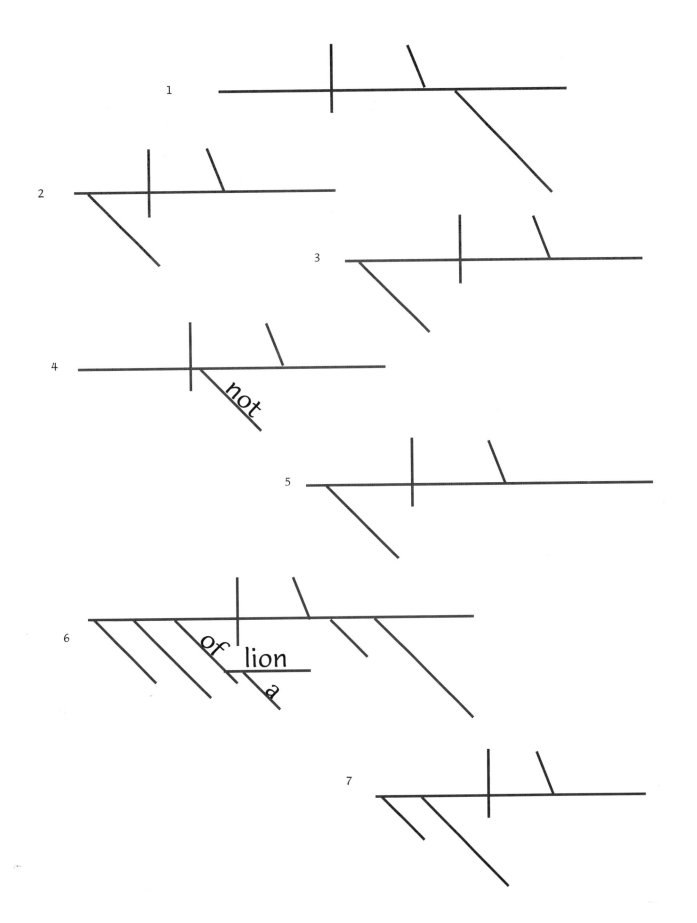

Now try these sentences which mix verbs of being with vebs having direct objects.

[1]Most planes carry heavy engines. [2]The Gossamer Condor is a very light plane. [3]Its pilot provides its power. [4]He pedals it. [5]What a light engine that is!

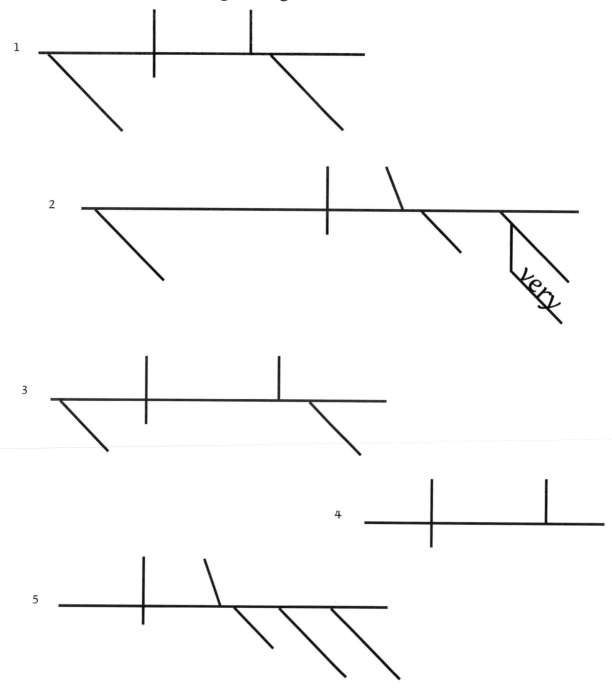

Now compose your own sentences and diagram them. Use verbs of being -- am, is, are, was, were, be, been -- and also verbs that take direct objects.

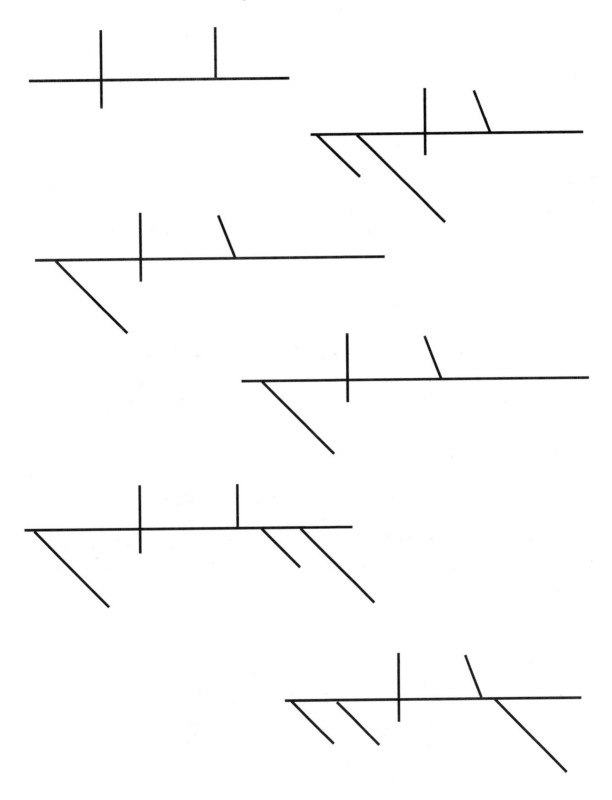

There are other linking verbs besides the verb "to be". Verbs of seeming and becoming are also linking verbs. Again, we have a word that seems to be a direct object because it answers the question, "Subject... verb... what?" but this word does not receive the action of the subject. It is just another name for it or a description of it. For example:

The rooster became my alarm clock.

The subject is "rooster"; the verb is "became". What did the rooster become? "My alarm clock". But this is not an action of the rooster; it's just another name for him. We diagram it the same way we diagram verbs of being:

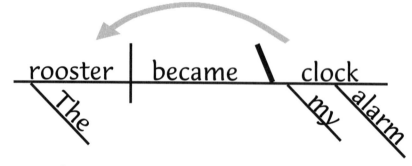

Similarly, we might say:

The eastern sky seems very dark.

What is the subject? What is the verb? What sort of verb is it? Is "dark" a direct object? Is it a noun? How would you diagram it?

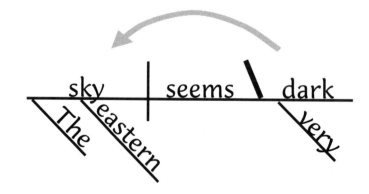

Here is a small story. It contains both linking verbs and non-linking verbs. First circle the linking verbs and underline the non-linking verbs. Then diagram the whole story. Add the lines you need for articles and adjectives.

¹The vole is a small meadow mammal. ²He looks mousy. ³He has sharp teeth. ⁴His nest is soft. ⁵He becomes thirsty. ⁶He visits a bright stream. ⁷His pathway is invisible. ⁸He seems shy. ⁹His hidden trail leads him. ¹⁰The trail's end is the fragrant orchard. ¹¹The gentle vole is happy.

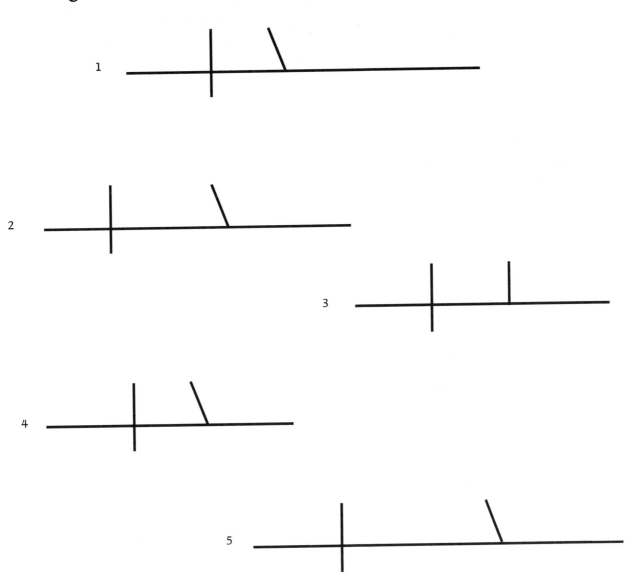

⁶He visits a bright stream. ⁷His pathway is invisible. ⁸He seems shy. ⁹His hidden trail leads him. ¹⁰The trail's end is the fragrant orchard. ¹¹The gentle vole is happy.

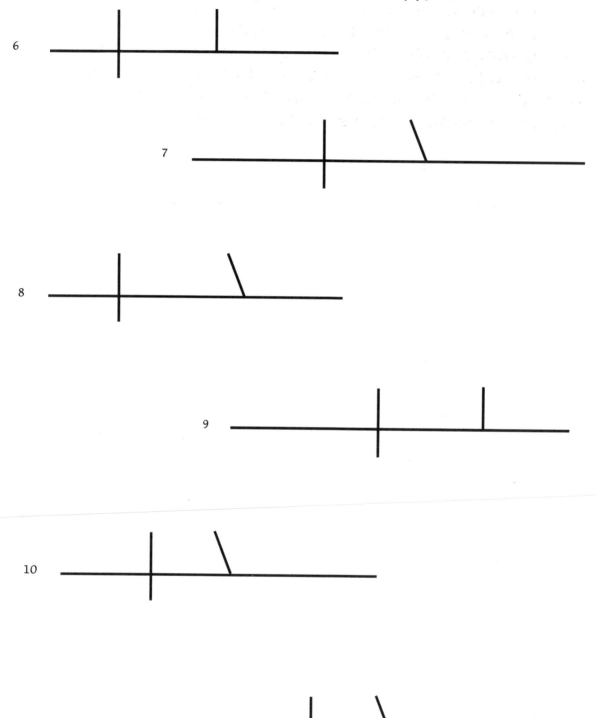

Verbs of sensing:

There is one more set of commonplace linking verbs. These are verbs of sensing — of touch, taste, and smell. These verbs can be confusing because sometimes they take direct objects; sometimes they merely link. Look at these sentences:

I smell a rat. The rat smells rotten.

In the first one, the rat receives the action of my smelling. In the second one, "rotten" is just an adjective for the smell. The verb "smell" is the same in both, but the <u>use</u> of the verb is different, — and the diagram is different:

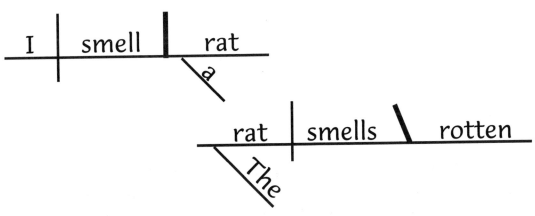

There are quite a number of these verbs that can be used either as links or with direct objects. If you are not sure what you have, here is a simple test: Substitute a form of the verb "to be" (that is, substitute: *am, is, are, was, were, be, will be, has been, have been,* or *had been* for the verb in the sentence.) If the meaning completely changes, you do not have a linking verb. If the meaning remains similar, you have a linking verb. Look at this pair of examples:

Luther Burbank grows Santa Rosa plums.
Santa Rosa plums grows large and sweet.

You can ask yourself two questions:
1) Is Luther Burbank a Santa Rosa plum?
2) Are Santa Rosa plums large and sweet?

Luther Burbank is <u>not</u> a plum! But his Santa Rosa plums are large and sweet. I'm sure you can finish the diagrams correctly, with a straight line in one circle and a slanted line in the other:

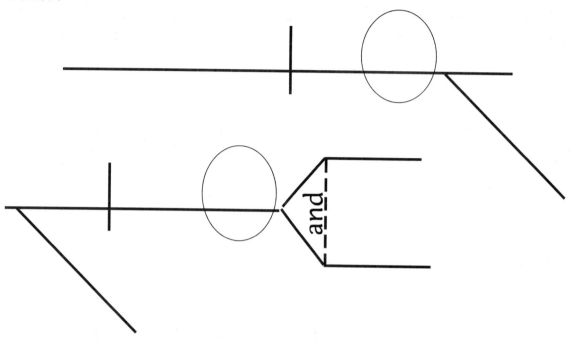

Here is a short story to challenge all you have learned so far about diagramming. Diagram each sentence, watching carefully for linking and non-linking verbs. The last two sentences have an unusual word order. Take them slowly. What is the verb? Who or what is doing the verb? I have put in the adverbs and prepositional phrases for you. We will study them in the next two chapters.

¹*It is Easter.* ²*The church has beautiful white lilies.* ³*I can smell them immediately.* [Note: "can smell" is the verb.] ⁴*They smell fresh.* ⁵*They look lovely.*
⁶*My baby smells one.* ⁷*Her nose touches the bright stamens.* ⁸*Yellow dust covers her nose.* ⁹*Now her nose is yellow.*
¹⁰*I feel a petal.* ¹¹*It feels smooth and cool.*
¹²*One blossom is droopy.* ¹³*Its single task is completed.* ¹⁴*Our task of worship remains.*
¹⁵*How gracious is the Lord!* ¹⁶*Let his house be ever beautiful!*

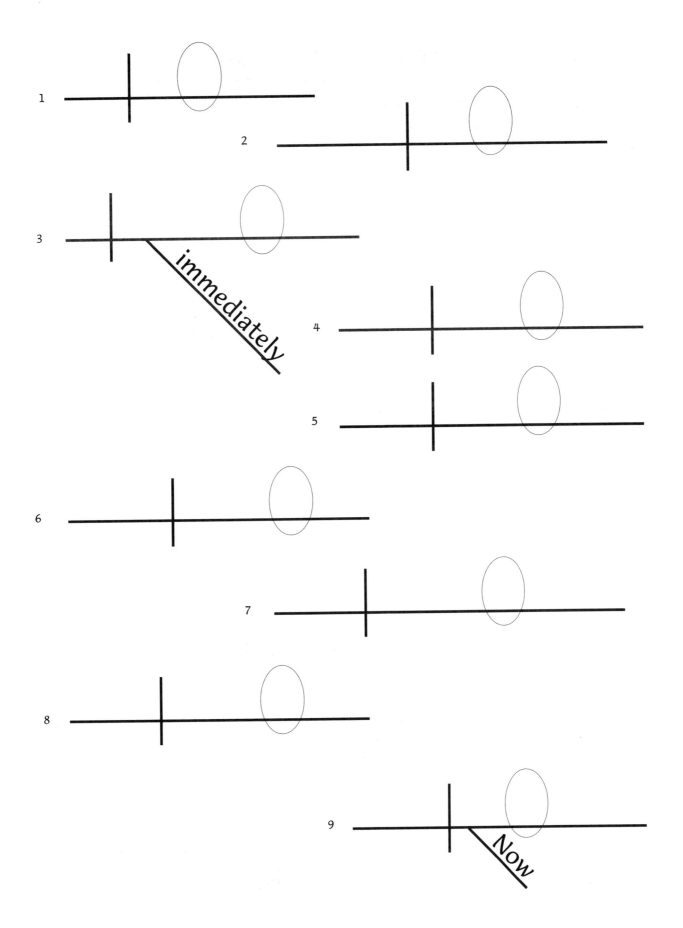

[10]I feel a petal. [11]It feels smooth and cool.
[12]One blossom is droopy. [13]Its single task is completed.
[14]Our task of worship remains.
[15]How gracious is the Lord! [16]Let his house be ever beautiful!

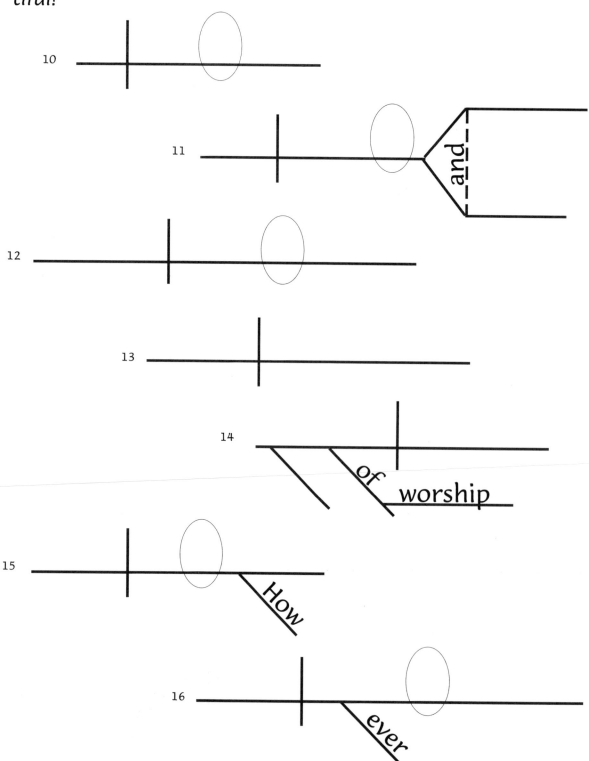

Chapter VI Adverbs:

In general, adverbs are words which describe verbs, adding something more specific to their meaning. Adverbs may also modify adjectives or other adverbs in a sentence. They describe the time, place, manner or cause of the action; or they mark the degree or intensity of the adjectives or adverbs.

Adverbs are identified by answering one of the following questions:

How? Why? When? Where? To what extent?

Like adjectives, adverbs are placed on slanted lines below the words they modify. If they modify verbs, this is simple; if they modify adjectives or adverbs which are already on slanted lines, they are placed on a slanted line below and parallel to the word they modify, and a small vertical line is drawn to connect the words. If you look back, you will find you have already seen several examples of adverbs (for example, see pages 38 and 45). Here are four new examples:

1) He came <u>quickly</u>. (He came how? He came <u>quickly</u>.)
2) I will go <u>tomorrow.</u> (I'll go when? I'll go <u>tomorrow</u>.)
       [Note: "will go" is the verb.]
3) She climbed <u>down</u>. (She climbed where? She climbed
       <u>down</u>.)
4) The paper is very strong. (To what extent is the paper strong? It is <u>very</u> strong.)

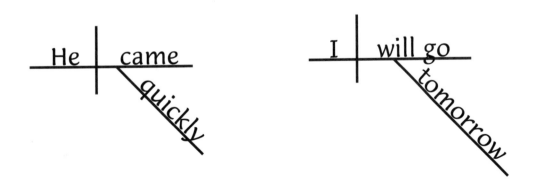

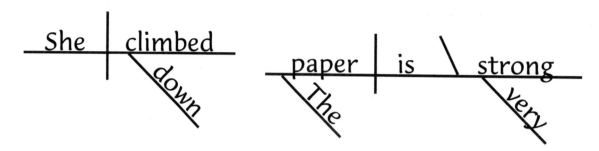

Read this familiar story from the diagram. Circle the adverbs and identify the question they answer. Notice that the word "not" is considered an adverb, because it qualifies the verb.

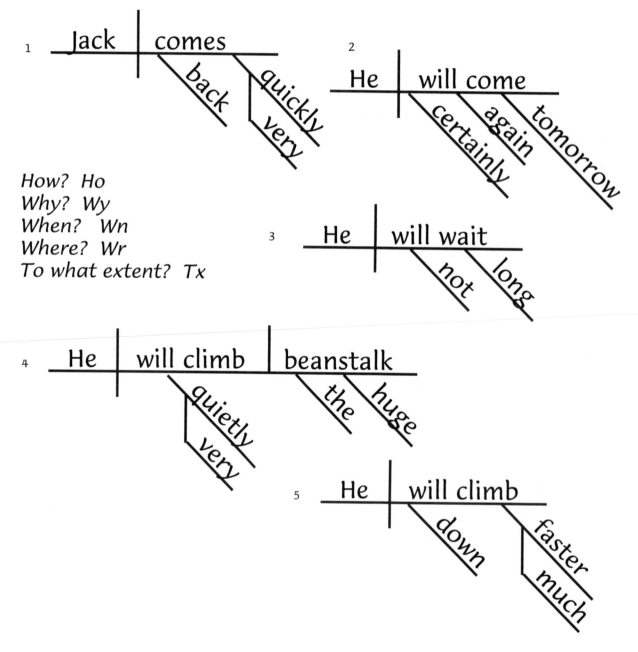

How? Ho
Why? Wy
When? Wn
Where? Wr
To what extent? Tx

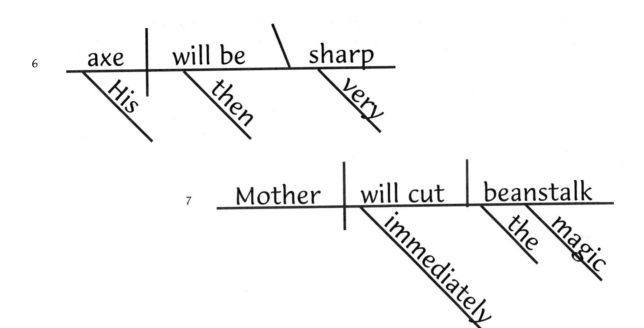

6 axe | will be \ sharp
His then very

7 Mother | will cut | beanstalk
immediately the magic

¹*Jack comes back very quickly.* ²*He will certainly come again tomorrow.* ³*He will not wait long.* ⁴*He will climb the huge beanstalk very quietly.* ⁵*He will climb down much faster.* ⁶*His axe will be very sharp then.* ⁷*Mother will cut the magic beanstalk immediately.*

DIAGRAMS AS MAPS

If you read the story from the diagram, you probably read the words in a slightly different order from the way I have written them in prose. Diagrams do not preserve or show the word order of a sentence; they only show the <u>syntactical relationships</u> between words.

Think of a map of a city. If you want to go somewhere, the map does not tell you to turn left first and right next. You can go left-then-right, or straight-then-left. Either way will get you there. The map only shows you the relationship between the streets.

Similarly, the diagram only shows you the relationship between the words. Your own sense of music and drama tells you which way to read them.

For your own practice, diagram the following sentences, full of adverbs. (I expect you can figure out the direct object lines yourself.)

[1]*America really needed some speedy help.* [2]*Old Ben Franklin bravely crossed the wide ocean.* [3]*He spoke urgently to the French.* [4]*Eventually, he returned happily.* [5]*French help would decisively assist our Revolution.*

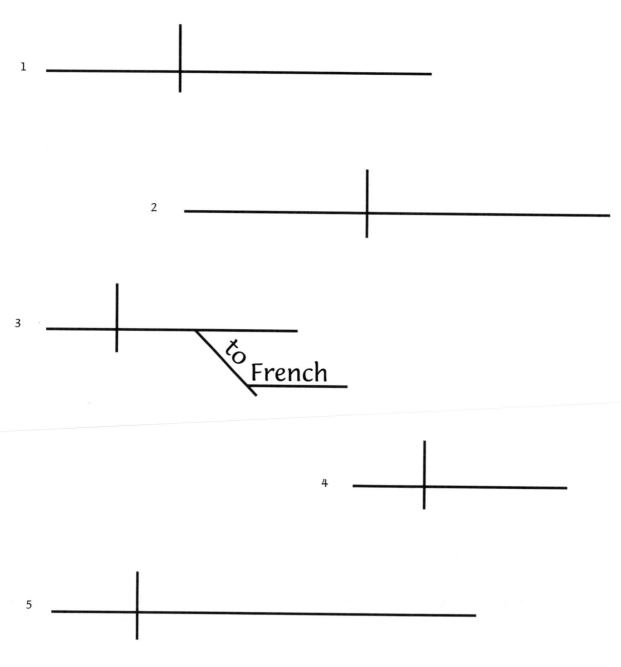

Do you know the carpenter's proverb?

¹The good carpenter measures carefully. ²He measures twice. ³He makes his cut exactly. ⁴Then his sharp saw whistles through. ⁵It cuts very quickly. ⁶The cut runs perfectly true.

⁷The careless carpenter measures once; then he cuts twice. ⁸His first cut always runs askew. ⁹Consequently, he must cut again. ¹⁰Carpenters always say, "measure once, cut twice; measure twice, cut once.

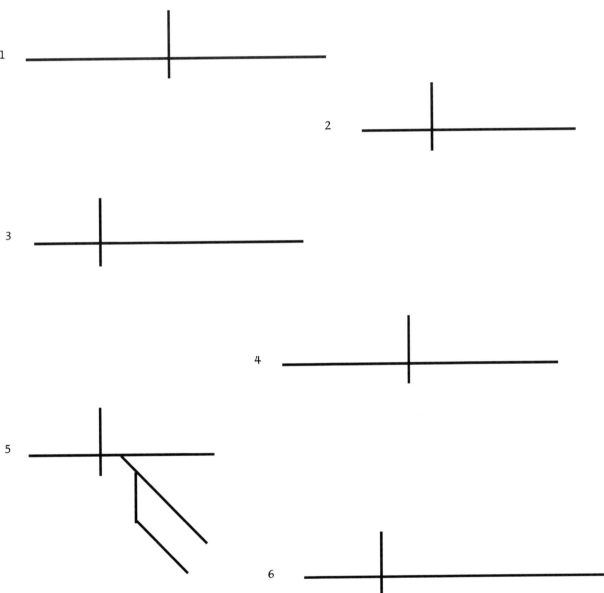

1

2

3

4

5

6

[7]The careless carpenter measures once; then he cuts twice. [8]His first cut always runs askew. [9]Consequently, he must cut again.

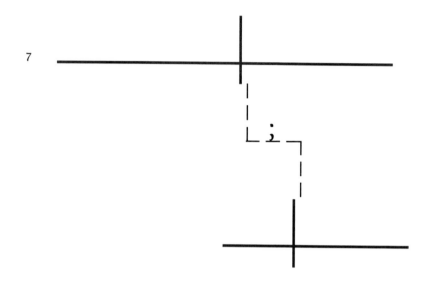

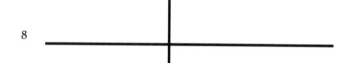

[10]Carpenters always say, "measure once, cut twice; measure twice, cut once."

The carpenter's proverb is in the form of an imperative sentence. The subject of an imperative sentence is "you" understood.

When we have a dialogue, of course, the whole thing that someone is saying is the direct object. We put it on a little tree. Can you finish this? (Don't forget the word "always".)

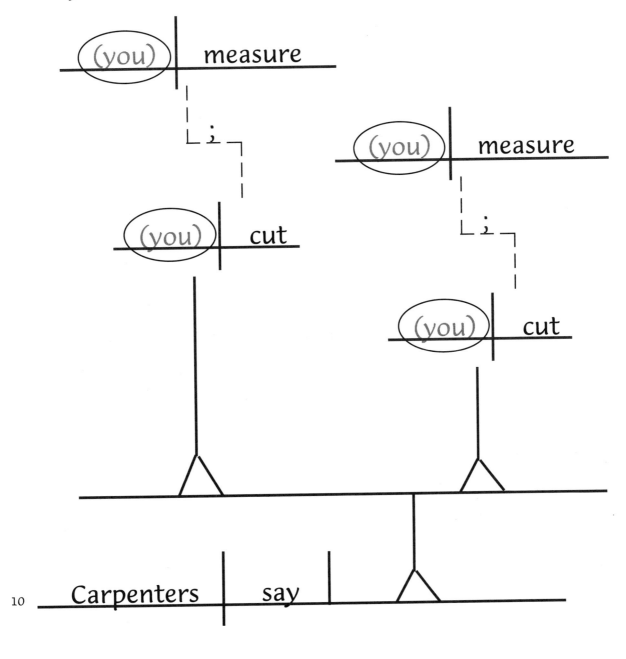

So now you can write your own sentences with adverbs of time, place, manner, and degree. There are not many single adverbs of cause. "Consequently" is the only one I can think of.

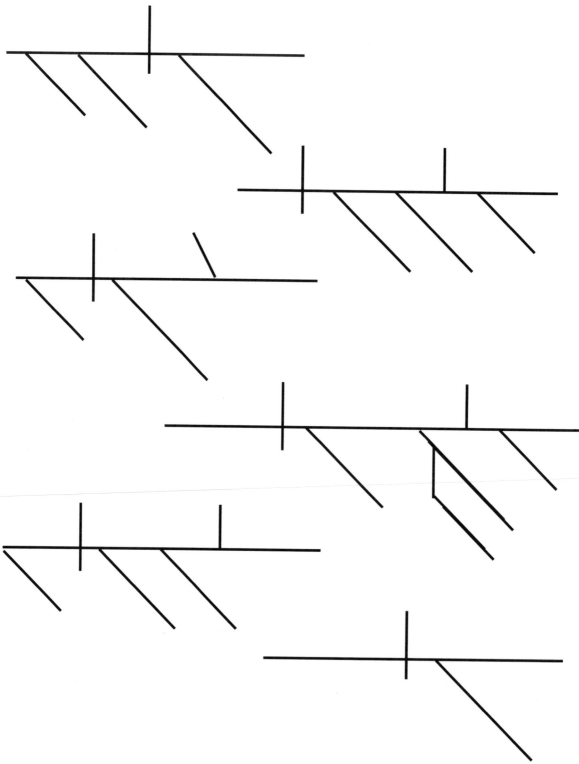

Chapter VII Prepositions

The preposition may be the hardest kind of word to explain. A preposition is not a word which names an idea or an action, nor does it describe or qualify anything. Instead, it expresses a _relationship_. A preposition is always followed by a noun, and it describes the _relationship_ between the thing named by this noun, and some other idea or action in the sentence.

A preposition may describe a relationship of position, such as:

¹_on_ the table
²_in_ the soup
³_under_ the stars
⁴_against_ the side
   (_of_ the house).

We diagram it like this:

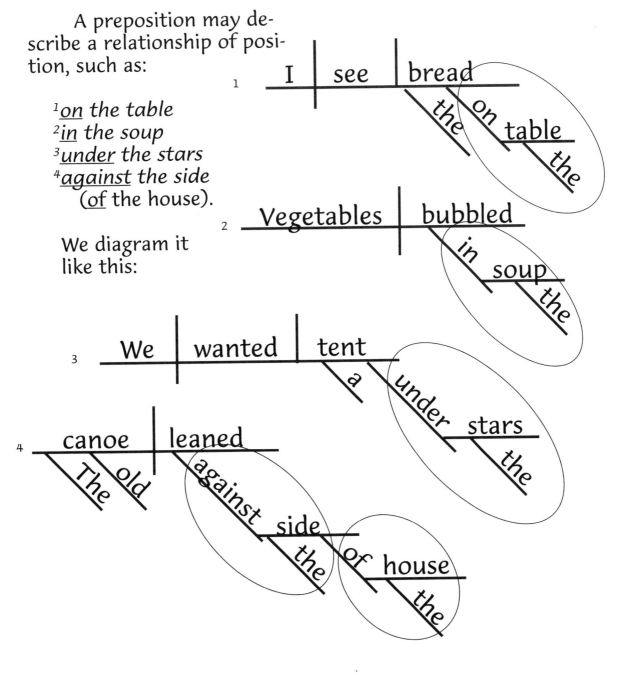

It may describe a family relationship or a relationship of possession such as:

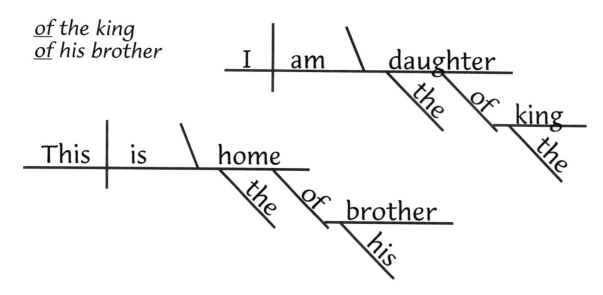

_of_ the king
_of_ his brother

DIAGRAM THESE SENTENCES WITH RELATIONSHIPS OF SEQUENCE:

[1] The day _before_ my graduation was so hectic.
[2] We went away _during_ the summer.
[3] America _after_ the Revolution was a new country.

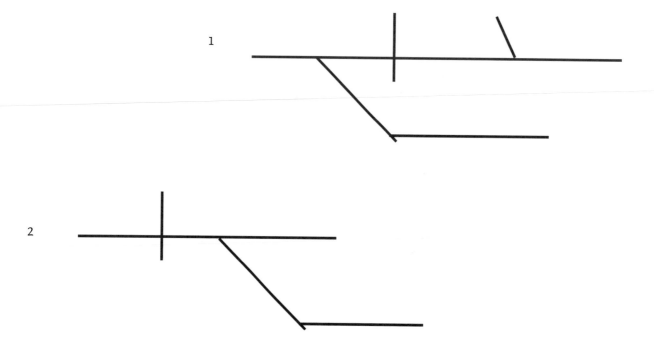

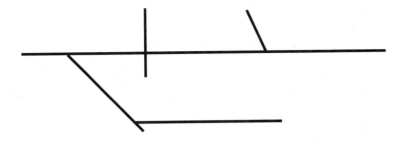

3

Would the sentence "After the Revolution, America was a new country," have the same diagram?

Some prepositions express a relationship of direction:

She went <u>into</u> the house.
They looked eagerly <u>towards</u> the mountain.

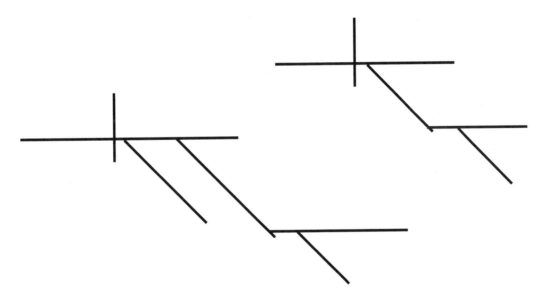

Or of purpose and cause:

Take this <u>for</u> your health.

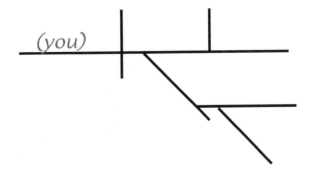

A preposition is thus always a part (the first word) of a prepositional phrase which includes a noun. In a diagram, we place the phrase underneath the word it is related to. The preposition itself goes on a slanted line; the noun in the phrase goes on a horizontal line; and any modifiers go below the noun as usual.

Looking back over the last two pages, you will see that some prepositional phrases modify nouns, some modify verbs. Therefore, some are adjectival and some are adverbial.

To place a prepositional phrase in a diagram, you need to see whether it is adverbial or adjectival, and you do this by checking whether it answers one of the questions,

"What kind, which one, whose, how many?"

-- which would make it adjectival, -- or one of the questions

"How, why, when, where?"

-- which would make it adverbial.

But this is not always enough, because, for example, a phrase which answers the question "Where?" may also answer the question, "Which one?" For example, "in the kitchen" may tell you where an action took place: "The girl worked in the kitchen;" or it may tell you which girl did it: "The girl in the kitchen brushes her hair very well." I certainly hope she does not brush it [where?] in the kitchen.

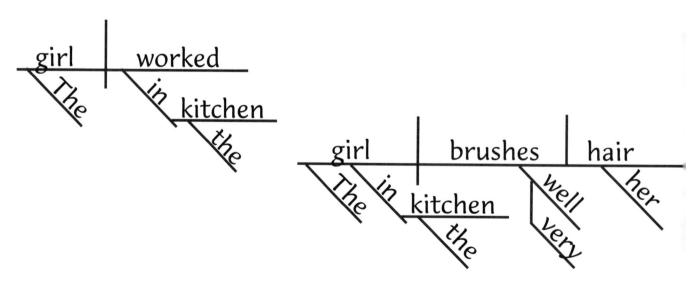

To properly place a prepositional phrase, find the noun or verb to which is it related. A noun will generally be right in front of its adjectival phrases; but adverbial phrases, like adverbs, may be at the beginning or end of a sentence, rather than near the verb. Confirm whether the <u>primary</u> intent of the phrase is to answer an adjectival question: "What kind? Which one? Whose, How many?" or an adverbial question: "How? Why? When? Where? To what extent?"

D<small>IAGRAM THESE SENTENCES</small>:

[1]*The book is on the table.* (<u>In this sentence</u>, does "on the table" answer the question "Which book?" or "Book is where?")
[2]*The book on the table is very interesting. (Same questions.)*
[3]*The book was written in French.* In this sentence, does the phrase "in French" answer the question "Which book?" or "Was written... how?"
[4]*The book in French is funny. (Same questions.)*

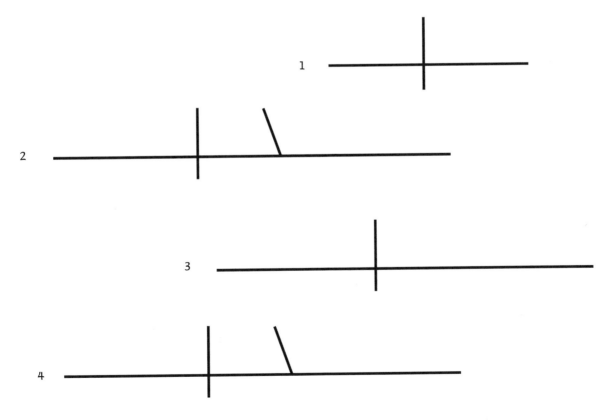

Even prepositions showing relationships of sequence may not always be adverbial, answering the question, "When?" Prove this to yourself by diagramming the following sentence pairs:

⁵The month before your visit went slowly.
⁶I finished my work before your visit.

⁷After a storm, we appreciate the gentle rainbow.
⁸The sky after a storm fills with golden light.

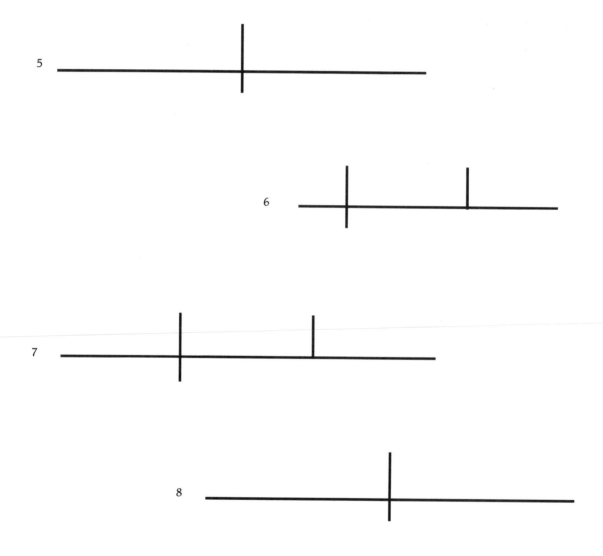

Here is a mix of prepositional phrases, some adverbial, some adjectival, answering the various adverbial and adjectival questions. Think carefully about both the question and the word for which the prepositional phrase answers that question and expresses the true _relationship._

¹America grew quickly after the revolution. ²The colonies along the Atlantic spread from that coastline, past the mountains, across the plains, and towards the western ocean. ³People of various nations came across the sea to the new country for many reasons.

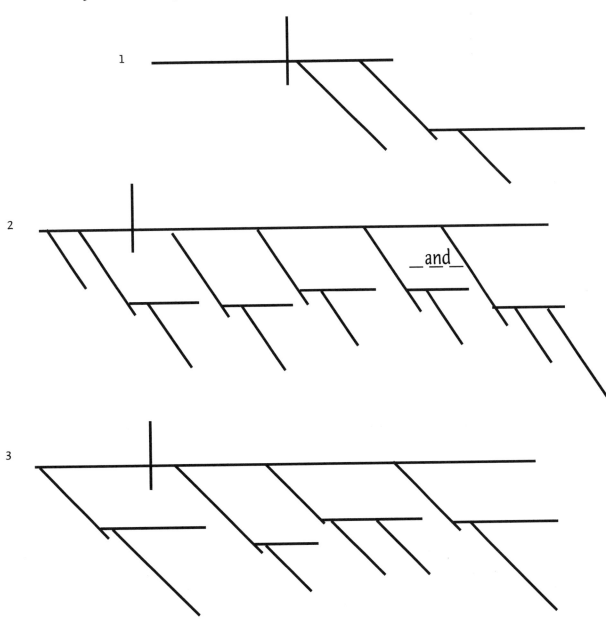

[4]Some came for the hope of religious freedom. [5]Some sought prosperity in the new land. [6]Some of the most adventurous seemed merely the restless children of a smaller continent. [7]Many of them would build homes for their families, in an unsettled wilderness, amidst political turmoil.

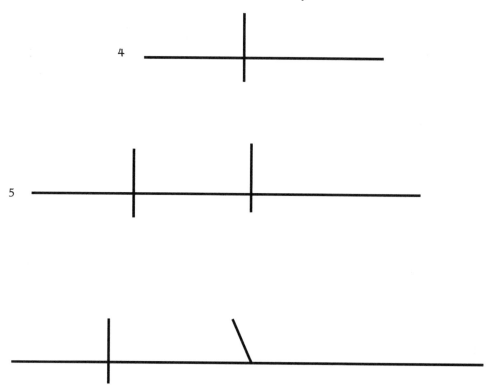

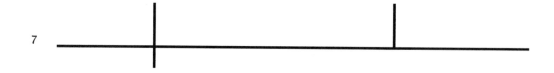

Watch! Do these prepositonal phrases go with the noun directly in front?

As the number of variables increases, it becomes more and more difficult to provide a useful template; you need to get another sheet of paper. Here are two pages of templates for dictated or composed sentences with prepositional phrases:

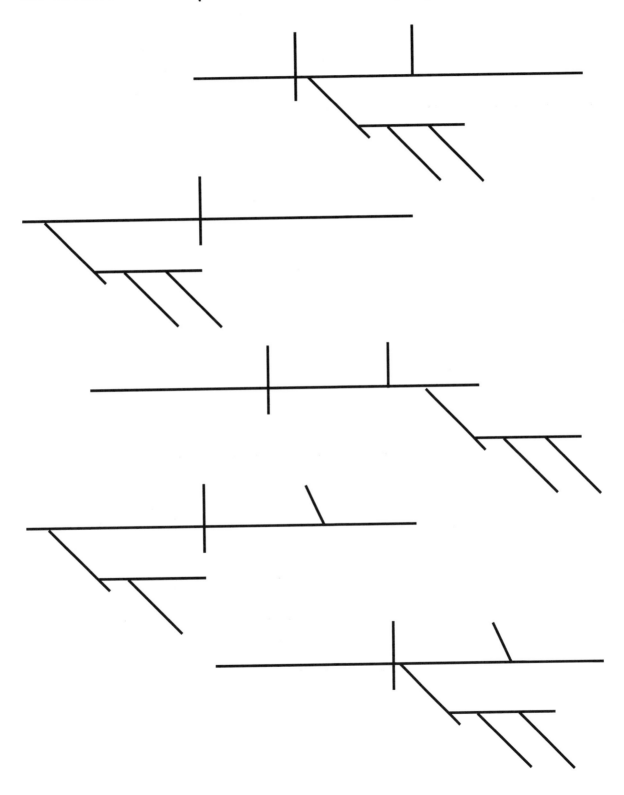

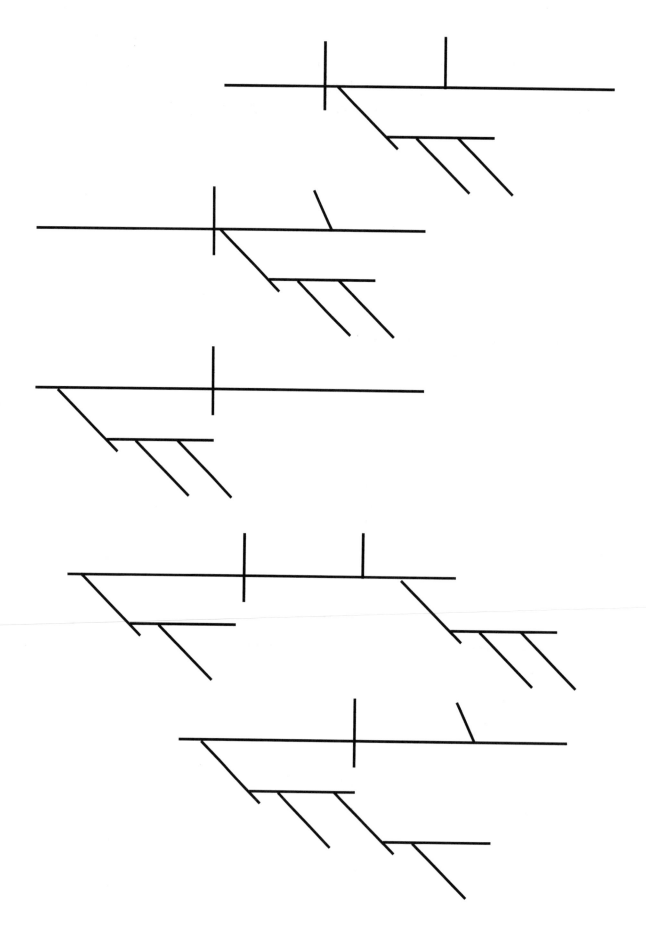

Chapter VIII A Peek Ahead

The parts of speech we have discussed -- noun and verb, -- article, adjective, and adverb, -- and preposition, -- are the raw materials for the syntactical units, the building blocks, of sentences. Nouns make subjects and direct objects; verbs make the center of the predicate, and so forth. Interjections, which just have a footnote on page 28, are a very simple addition. Pronouns, which we have used but not discussed, are -- in diagrams -- treated exactly the same way as nouns.

There is just one more thing. We need conjunctions, both to mark various listings, as we have already done from time to time (see page 21-23, for example) but also to introduce sub-thoughts, using subordinate clauses, which are often essential to the clear expression of the main thought.

What is a clause? A clause is a syntactic unit which has a subject and a predicate. It may stand by itself as a simple sentence, or it may be a part of a larger sentence with other clauses. Remember what we said at the start:

A sentence is a sequence of words whose relationships express a unit of thought.

Sometimes an idea expressed in the main clause of a sentence must be understood against the background of another idea, expressed in another clause. For example, I might say:

I came when he called.

There are two clauses here, and each could be an independent sentence, leaving out the word "when." I could say,

I came.
He called.

But something is left out when I put it that way. The essential <u>relationship</u> between the two ideas is expressed by the word "when" <u>and by their combination into a single sentence.</u>

A sentence which has a principal clause and a dependent clause is called a complex sentence. The meaning of a complex sentence depends on the relationship between its clauses.

In this final chapter, I want to give just a peek at the complex sentence. Then you really will have enough tools to diagram most of what you say.

Let's begin with the sentence already given:

I came when he called.

Here is the diagram, and the slanted line below the verb indicates that the entire clause is adverbial, answering the adverbial question, "When?"

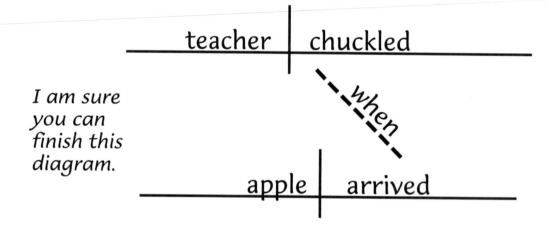

Now I want you to reflect on a possibly surprising fact. <u>Structurally considered,</u> the above sentence is not very different from many longer ones such as this:

Our sweet new teacher chuckled merrily
when her bright red apple arrived in a big bucket.

I am sure you can finish this diagram.

Having done that, you see that you need not be intimidated by numerous words, and can readily diagram this sentence:

When the nuts ripened amidst the high dense foliage, the young squirrels chased each other merrily through the branches of the walnut tree.

Think about the meaning of the words. Which clause is introduced by the word "when"? Remember that word order is not preserved in diagrams! I have given you some of the lines, but not all of them.

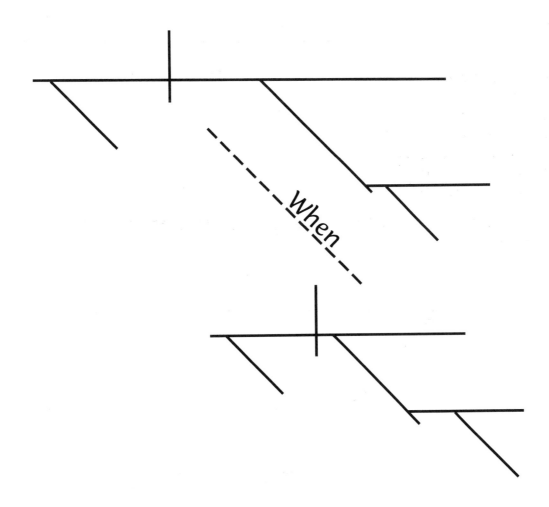

The dependent clauses we have been looking at are all adverbial. There can also be adjectival clauses, answering the usual adjectival questions: what kind, which one, whose, how many? For example:

Leaves <u>*which are composed of several leaflets*</u> *are called compound leaves.*

Note that the word "which" is a pronoun, the subject, in the clause, "which are composed of several leaflets."

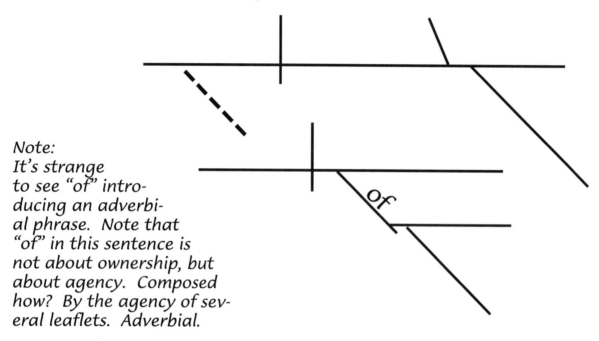

Note:
It's strange
to see "of" intro-
ducing an adverbi-
al phrase. Note that
"of" in this sentence is
not about ownership, but
about agency. Composed
how? By the agency of sev-
eral leaflets. Adverbial.

Now try this: *Leaves which have paired leaflets are pinnately compound.*

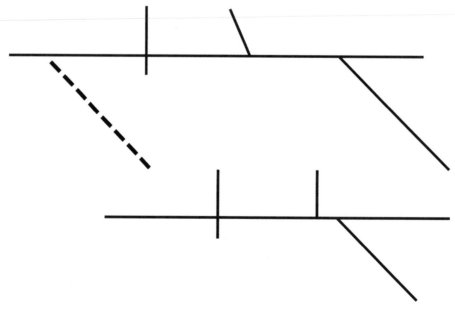

There can be clauses used as nouns, introduced by a "that" which sits above the diagram, since it has no place in any clause:

That leaves can be doubly pinnate is truly wondrous.

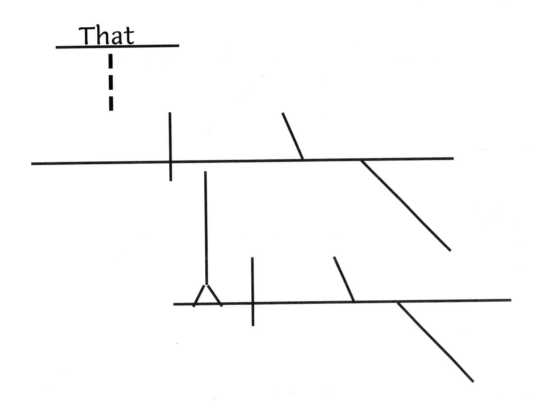

And of course, a sentence can have several subordinate clauses. Here is a sentence with a noun clause for the subject and an adverbial clause answering the question, "Why?"

That many ferns must be called triply pinnate is now clear, for they have doubly pinnately compound leaflets.

Try it by yourself on other paper, and then turn the page for some helpful lines.

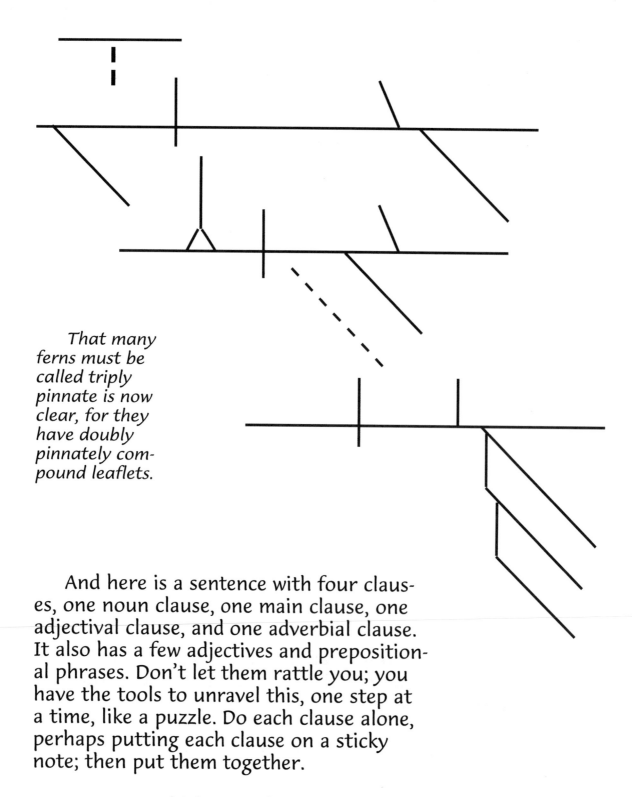

That many ferns must be called triply pinnate is now clear, for they have doubly pinnately compound leaflets.

And here is a sentence with four clauses, one noun clause, one main clause, one adjectival clause, and one adverbial clause. It also has a few adjectives and prepositional phrases. Don't let them rattle you; you have the tools to unravel this, one step at a time, like a puzzle. Do each clause alone, perhaps putting each clause on a sticky note; then put them together.

Leaves, which provide necessary oxygen for us, show that important works may be done humbly, for they are wholly commonplace.

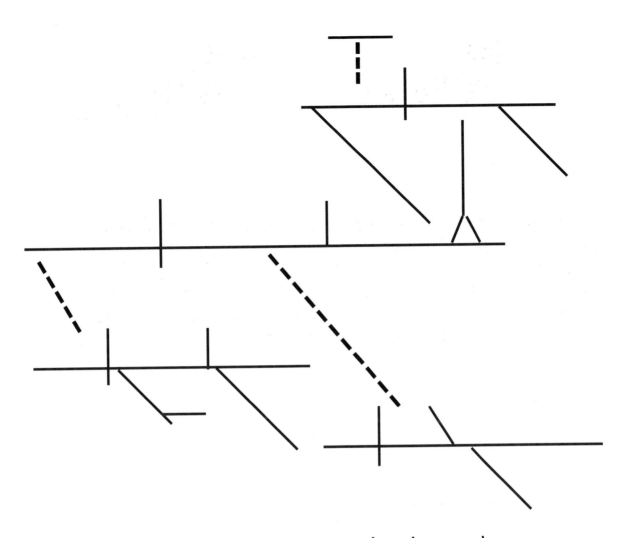

Have you noticed that nouns and verbs are always on horizontal lines while adjectives, adverbs, and prepositions are on slanted lines?

What do you suppose happens when a verb is used as an adjective, as in "the whistling wind?" "Whistling" is a part of the verb "whistle," yet in this phrase, it is used as an adjective for "wind." Some people put such words on a curved line; some use a stairstep. I use a curve because that is what I learned in school and I think that is an expressive shape for these hybrid words. I'm guessing that those who use a stair-step are responding to drawing and typesetting problems. Either way, we place the word "whistling" under its noun, "wind," on a line that suggests a hybrid between a slant and a horizontal line, indicating the syntactic combination of adjective and verb.

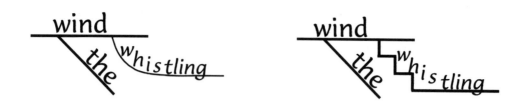

There are many more things to learn, some of which you can find in <u>The First Whole Book of Diagrams</u>. One edition of this book is called <u>The Complete Book of Diagrams</u>, but I doubt that a book of diagrams can ever be complete because the complexity of human thought is never exhausted. Certainly the fascination of mapping syntax in our beautiful language never comes to an end.

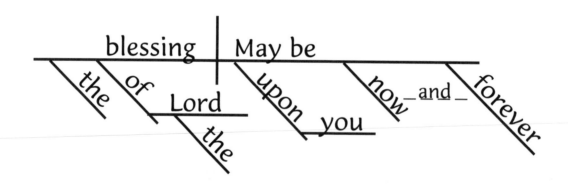

The capital "M" tells you which is supposed to be the first word in the sentence.

Answer Key
for Diagramming Worktext

Diagrams for page 5

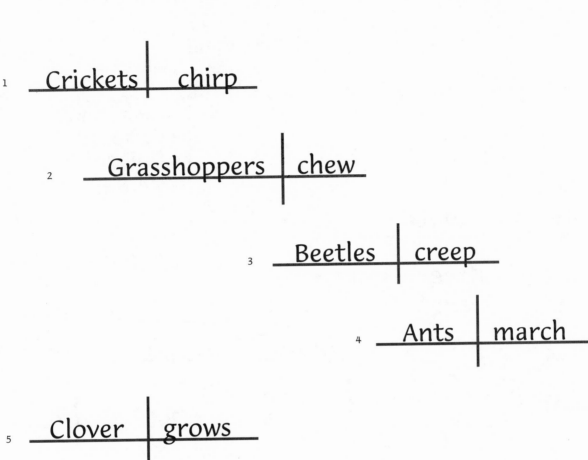

1. Crickets | chirp

2. Grasshoppers | chew

3. Beetles | creep

4. Ants | march

5. Clover | grows

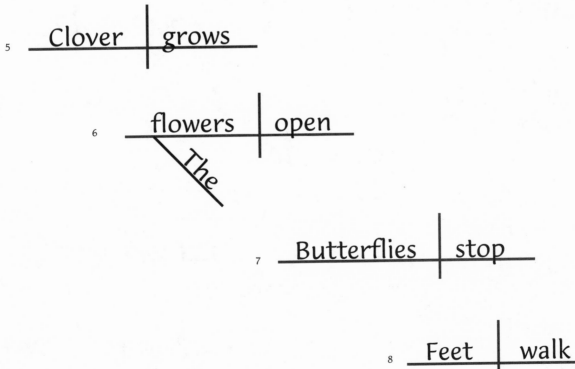

6. flowers | open
   The

7. Butterflies | stop

8. Feet | walk

Diagrams for page 10

The Orchard

[1]Spring comes.
[2]The trees bud.
[3]The blossoms open.
[4]The bees visit.
[5]The wind blows.
[6]The petals fall.
[7]The fruit grows.
[8]The children come.

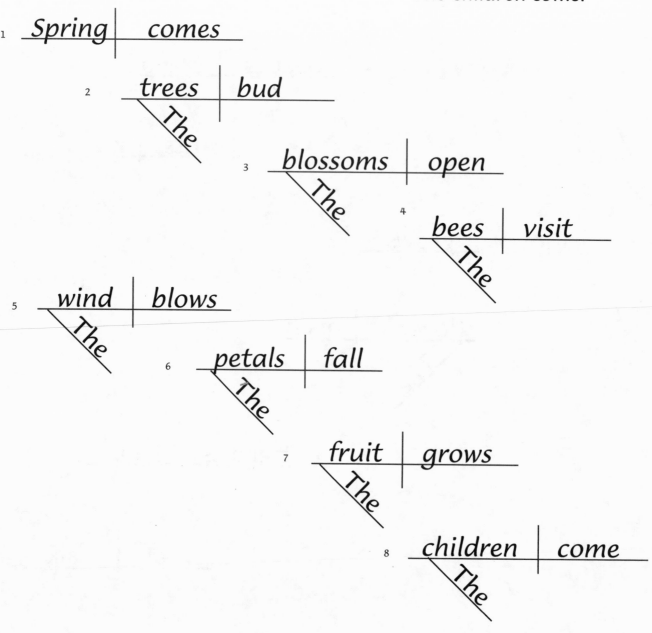

Diagrams for page 12-13

The Acorn

[1]Springtime comes. [2]An oak grows. [3]The acorns ripen. [4]A wind roars. [5]The acorns fall. [6]A squirrel comes. [7]He chatters. [8]He eats. [9]The acorns disappear. [10]The leaves fall. [11]The acorns hide. [12]A snowstorm passes. [13]Spring returns. [14]An acorn sprouts. [15]An oak grows. [16]The acorns ripen...

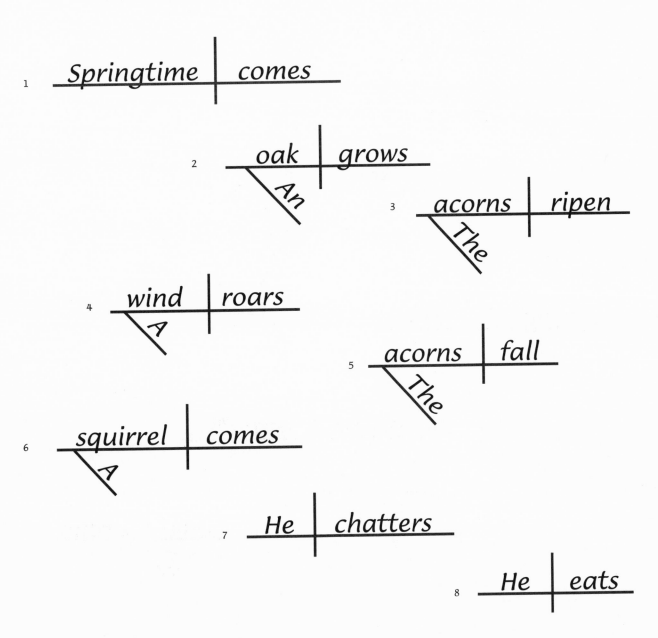

The Acorn continued for pages 12-13:

[9]The acorns disappear.
[10]The leaves fall.   [11]The acorns hide.
[12]A snowstorm passes.
[13]Spring returns.   [14]One acorn sprouts.   [15]An oak grows.

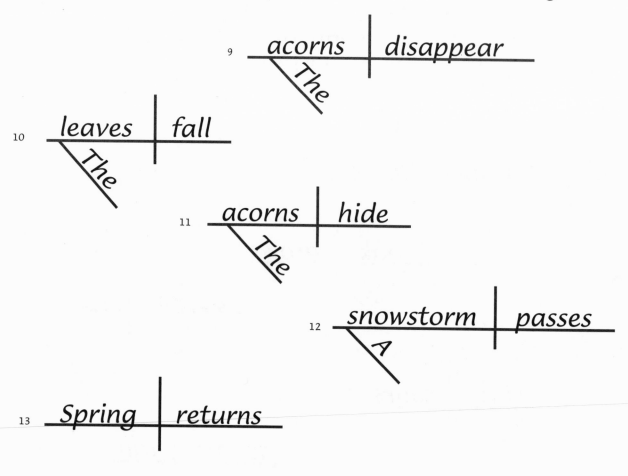

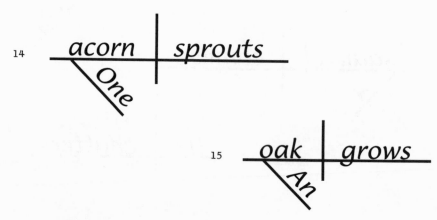

Diagrams for page 14

The Fledgling

[1]An eaglet looks. [2]He hops. [3]The little wings flutter.
[4]The fledgling tumbles.
[5]The mother comes. [6] A great wing appears.
[7]The eaglet is caught.

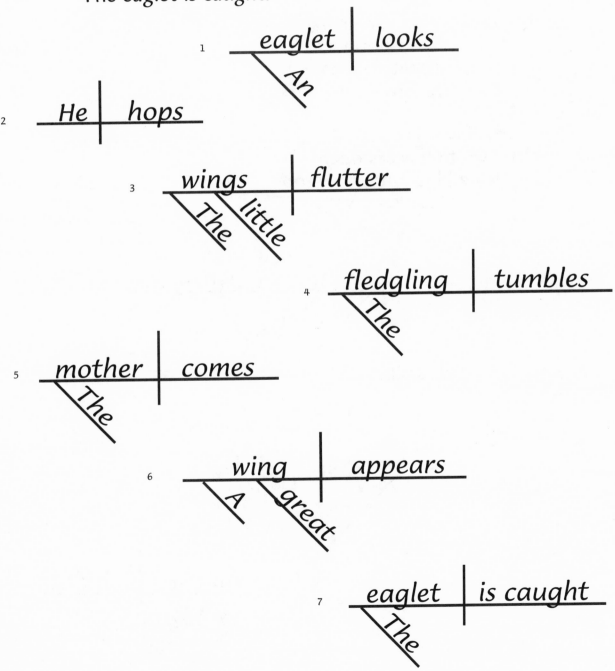

Diagrams for pages 18-19

<u>In the Grass II</u>

[1]The gentle wind whispers.
[2]The golden sun shines.
[3]Little snakes slither.
[4]A quick mouse hides.

[5]The musical crickets chirp.
[6]The hungry grasshoppers chew.
[7]A shiny beetle creeps.
[8]The busy ants work.

[9]The rich clover grows.
[10]Little white flowers open.
[11]One blue butterfly stops.
[12]*Bare* feet walk.

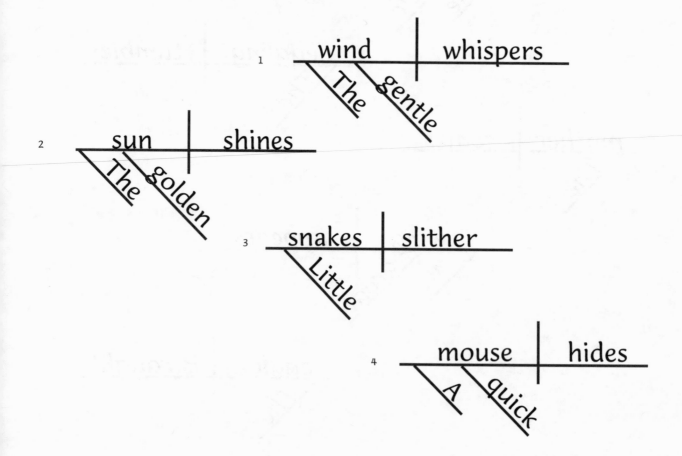

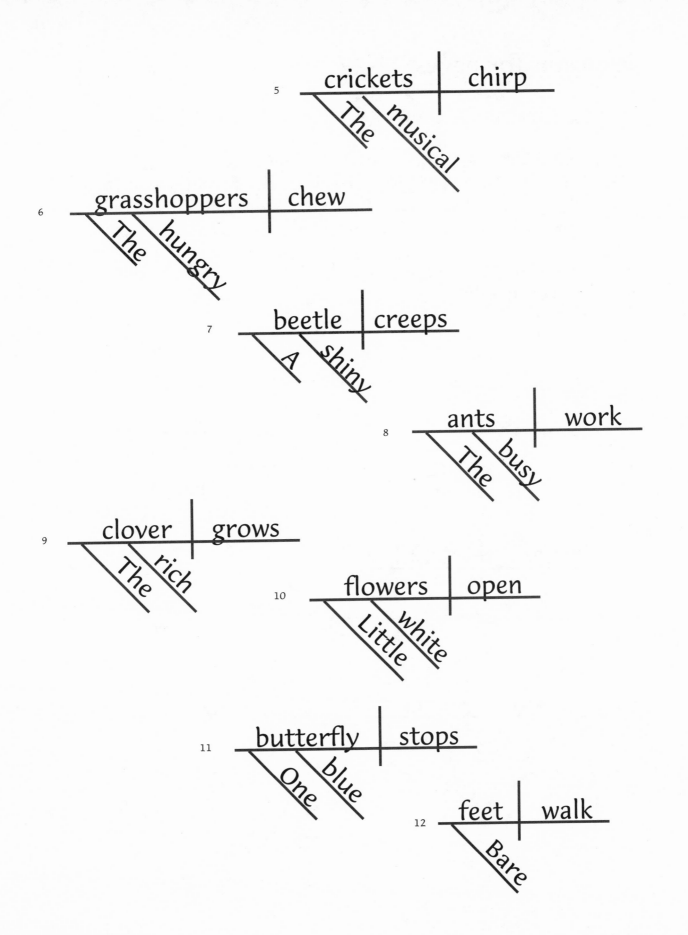

Diagrams for pages 22-23

The Elephant's Child

[1]The elephants's child wonders. [2]He asks and asks.
[3]His tired mother scolds. [4]His grouchy father scowls.
[5]The tall ostrich kicks. [6]The hairy baboon chatters.
[7]The curious elephant travels. [8]His many questions continue.
[9]The crafty crocodile whispers. [10]The elephant listens, and the crocodile bites.
[11]The elephant's nose stretches!

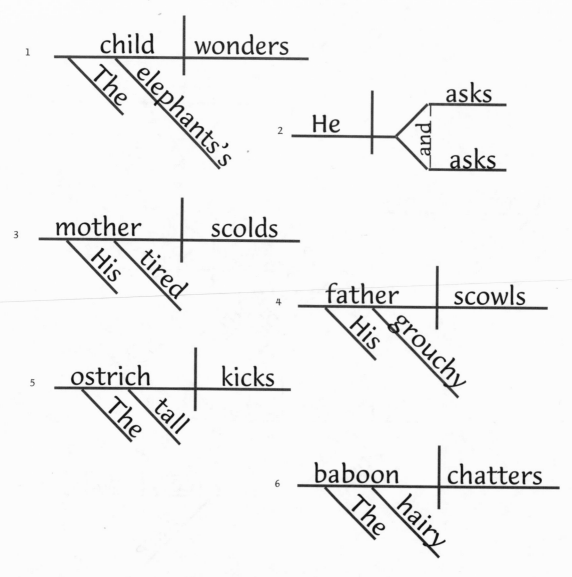

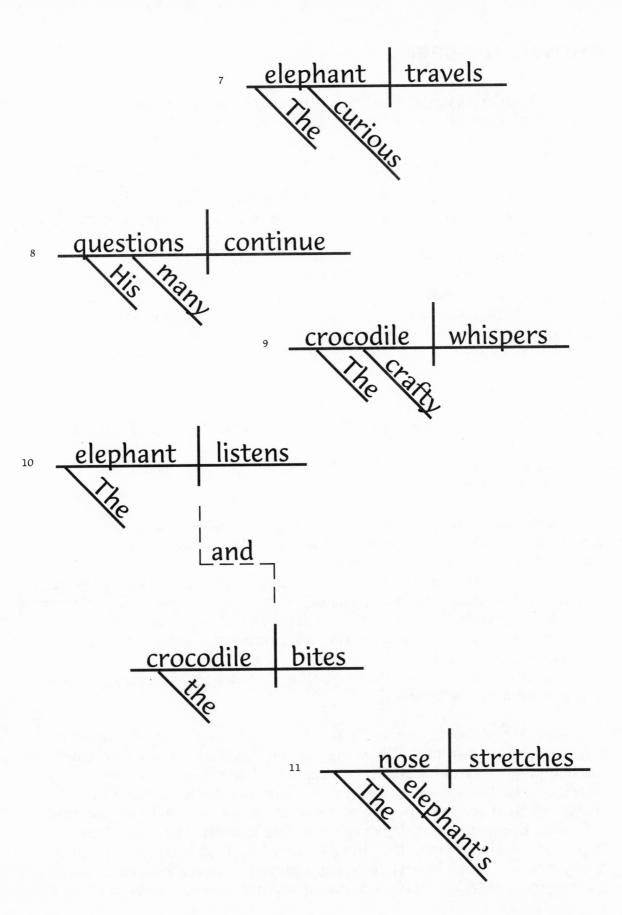

7   elephant | travels

The   curious

8   questions | continue

His   many

9   crocodile | whispers

The   crafty

10   elephant | listens

The

and

crocodile | bites

the

11   nose | stretches

The   elephant's

Answers for page 25

1) Sarah drinks <u>milk</u>. "Milk" is a noun, the direct object.

Sarah can <u>milk</u> the cow. "Milk" is a verb, something Sarah does to the cow.

<u>Milk</u> soup with pepper is good for a sick child. "Milk" is an adjective, modifying the noun "soup."

2) The <u>desert</u> is dry. "Desert" is a noun, the subject of the sentence.

The <u>desert</u> flowers are brilliant. "Desert" is an adjective, modifying flowers.

3) Ann enjoys <u>travel</u>. "Travel" is a noun, the direct object.

She will <u>travel</u> by plane. "Travel" is a verb, part of the simple predicate, "will travel."

The <u>travel</u> agent will help. "Travel" is an adjective, describing the type of agent who will help.

4) The <u>red</u> light is the stoplight. "Red" is an adjective, modifying "light."

<u>Red</u> means stop. "Red" is a noun, called a substantive.

5) The <u>tree</u> is very tall. "Tree" is a noun.

The <u>tree</u> trunk is rough. "Tree" is an adjective, modifying the noun "trunk."

My dog can <u>tree</u> any cat in the neighborhood. "Tree" is a verb, what the dog does to the cat.

Nouns are naming words; they can be the subject of a sentence, the direct object, the object of a preposition, or a few other things, but as long as they name something, they are nouns.

Verbs are action words, or perhaps words of being. A verb is the centerpiece of the predicate in a sentence.

Noun and verb are grammar terms; subject, direct object, and predicate are syntax terms. Syntax is the description of a word <u>as used in a particular sentence.</u>

Adjectives are descriptive words. The word adjective is both a grammatical and a syntactic term.

Most English books explain that a noun is a naming word and then give, or ask for, examples. Then they explain that a verb is an action word, and give examples. It is very important to understand that many words are used in a variety of ways. A noun may begin as the name of a thing and then become also the name of an action -- a verb -- associated with that thing. Conversely, a verb may begin as an action word, and then become the name of the thing achieved by that action. Take time to understand that when we diagram a sentence we see how each word is used <u>in this sentence</u>. The usual nouns are not always nouns, are they?

Diagrams for page 24

4) The <u>red</u> light is the stoplight.
Red means stop.
5) The <u>tree</u> is very tall.
The <u>tree</u> trunk is rough.
My dog can <u>tree</u> any cat in the neighborhood.

Note: the slanted line after "is" will be explained in chapter 5 -- coming up!

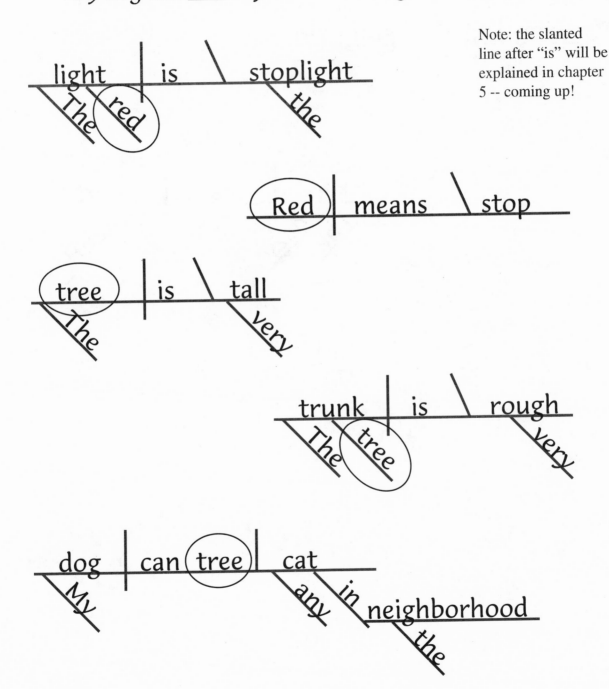

Diagrams for page 27

Peter's wife likes pumpkins
The hazy skies make gentle colors.

Diagrams for page 30

The naughty little rabbit ate all my lettuce.

The simple subject is "rabbit".
The complete subject is "the naughty little rabbit".
The verb, or simple predicate, is "ate".
The direct object is "lettuce".
The complete predicate is "ate all my lettuce".

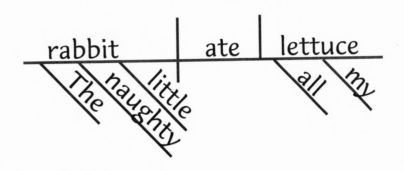

The rugged old fishermen cast their great nets.

The simple subject is "fishermen".
The complete subject is "the rugged old fishermen".
The verb, or simple predicate, is "cast".
The direct object is "nets".
The complete predicate is "cast their great nets".

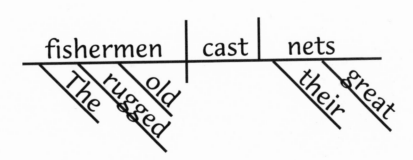

Diagrams for page 31

The morning sun brightens the pale sandstone.

The simple subject is "sun".
The complete subject is "the morning sun".
The verb, or simple predicate, is "brightens".
The direct object is "sandstone".
The complete predicate is "brightens the pale sandstone".

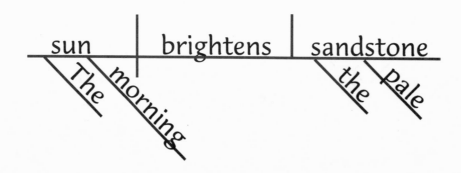

A thousand spider webs carried the bright morning dew.

The simple subject is "webs".
The complete subject is "a thousand spider webs".
The verb, or simple predicate, is "carried".
The direct object is "dew". (Ask: webs carried what?)
The complete predicate is "carried the bright morning dew".

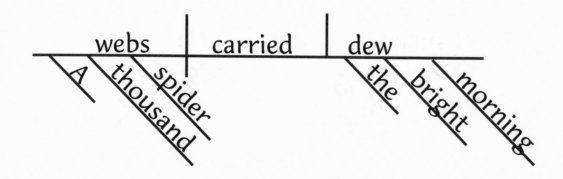

Diagrams for page 32

[1]The sturdy pine trees produce cones.
[2]The brown cones have little scales.
[3]These scales hide tiny seeds.
[4]The busy squirrels and little birds find the seeds.
[5]One small seed hides and sprouts.

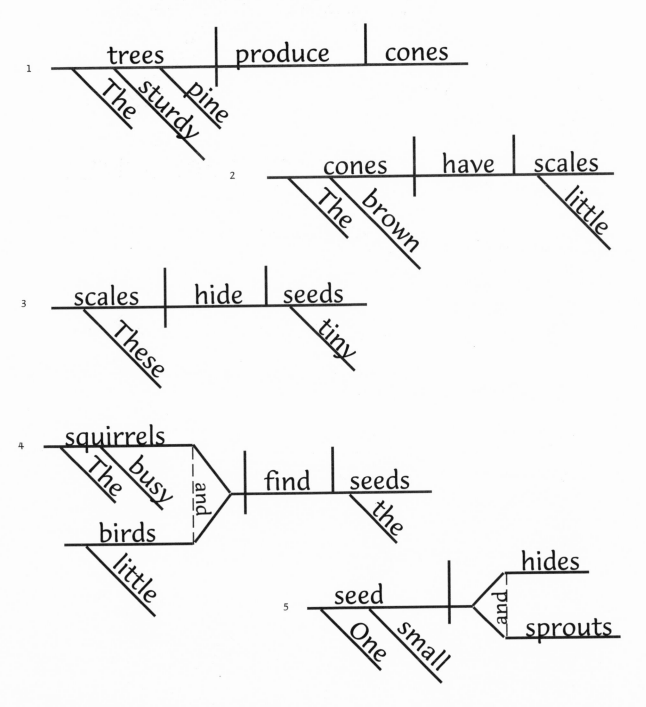

Diagrams for page 36-37

[1]Lions are beautiful creatures. [2]Their fur is golden.
[3]Their manes are long. [4]Lions are not gentle. [5]Their paws are enormous. [6]The great roar of a lion is a terrible sound. [7]A hungry lion is fierce.

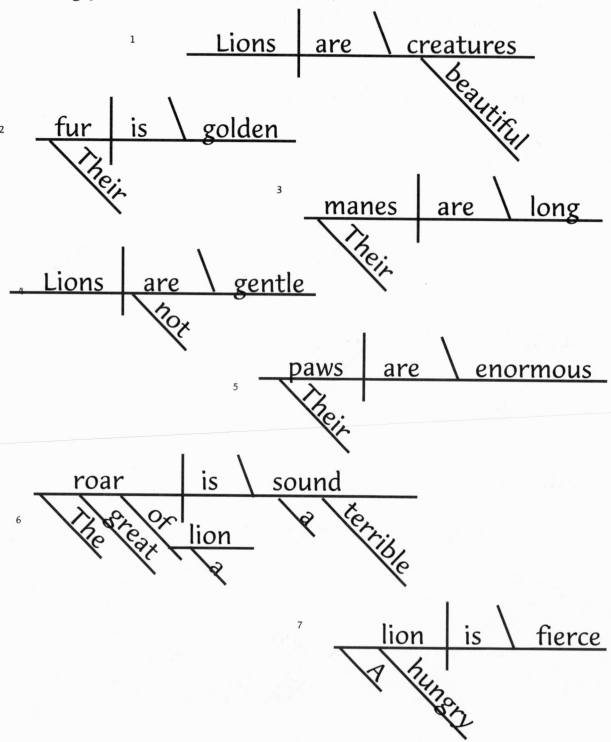

Diagrams for page 38-39

[1]Most planes carry heavy engines.　[2]The Gossamer Condor is a very light plane. [3]Its pilot provides its power. [4]He pedals it. [5]What a light engine that is!

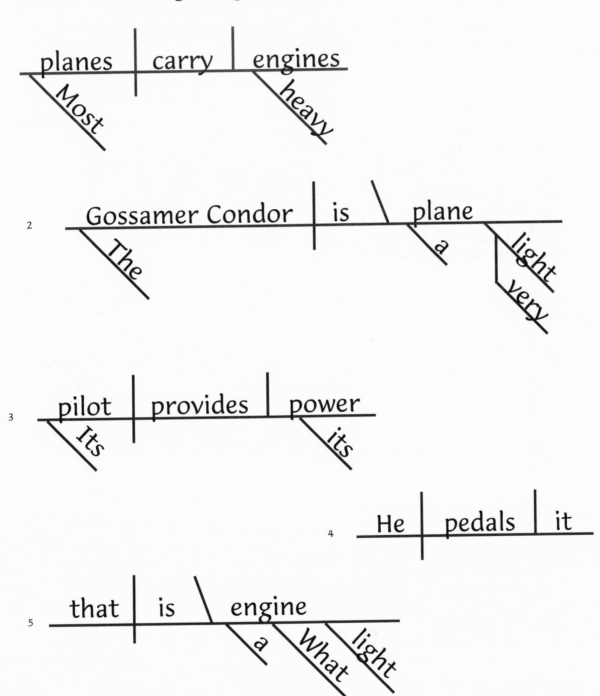

Diagrams for pages 41-42

[1]The vole is a small meadow mammal. [2]He looks mousy.
[3]He has sharp teeth. [4]His nest is soft. [5]He becomes thirsty.
[6]He visits a bright stream. [7]His pathway is invisible. [8]He seems
shy. [9]His hidden trail leads him. [10]The trail's end is the fragrant orchard. [11]The gentle vole is happy.

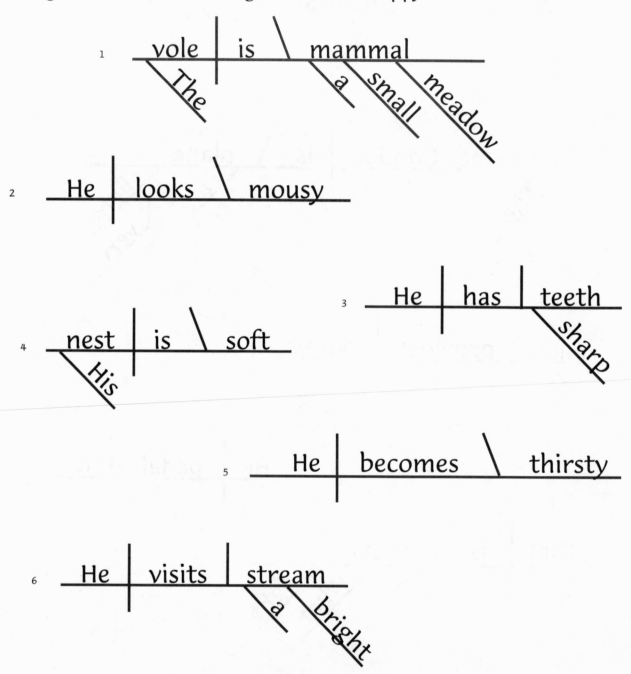

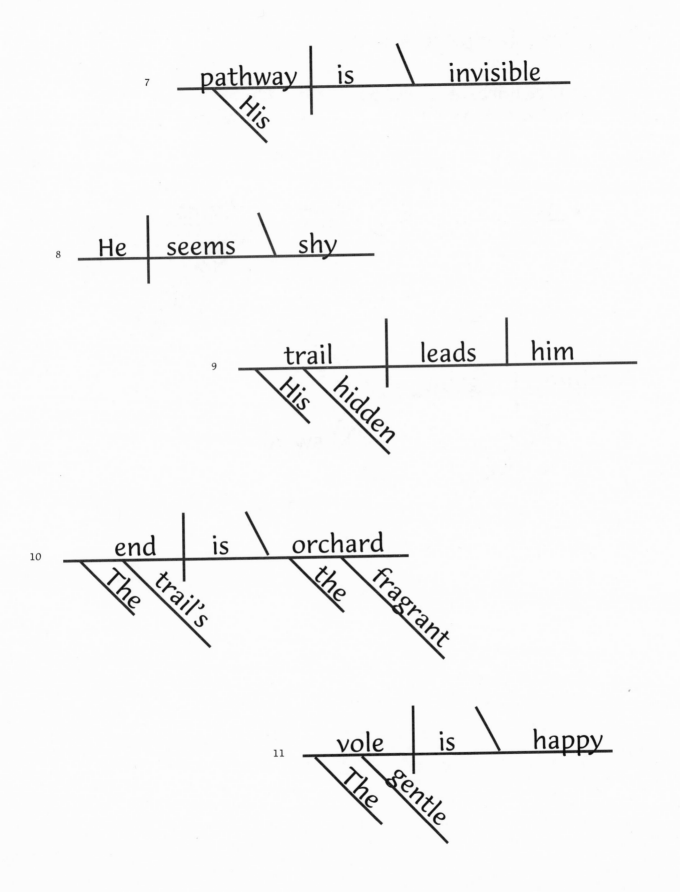

7

pathway | is \ invisible

His

8

He | seems \ shy

9

trail | leads | him

His   hidden

10

end | is \ orchard

The trail's   the fragrant

11

vole | is \ happy

The gentle

Diagrams for page 44

Luther Burbank grows Santa Rosa plums.
The Santa Rosa plum grows large and sweet.

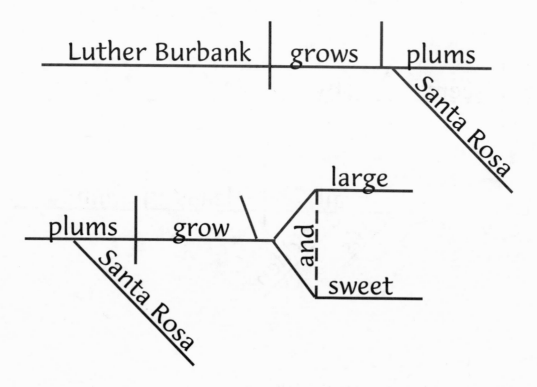

Diagrams for page 45-46

¹It is Easter. ²The church has beautiful white lilies. ³I can smell them immediately. ⁴They smell fresh. ⁵They look lovely.

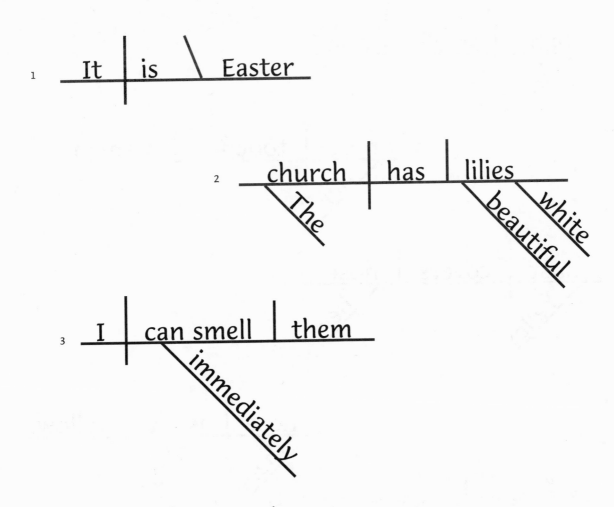

Continued -- for pages 45-46

[6]My baby smells one. [7]Her nose touches the bright stamens. [8]Yellow dust covers her nose. [9]Now her nose is yellow.
[10]I feel a petal. [11]It feels smooth and cool.

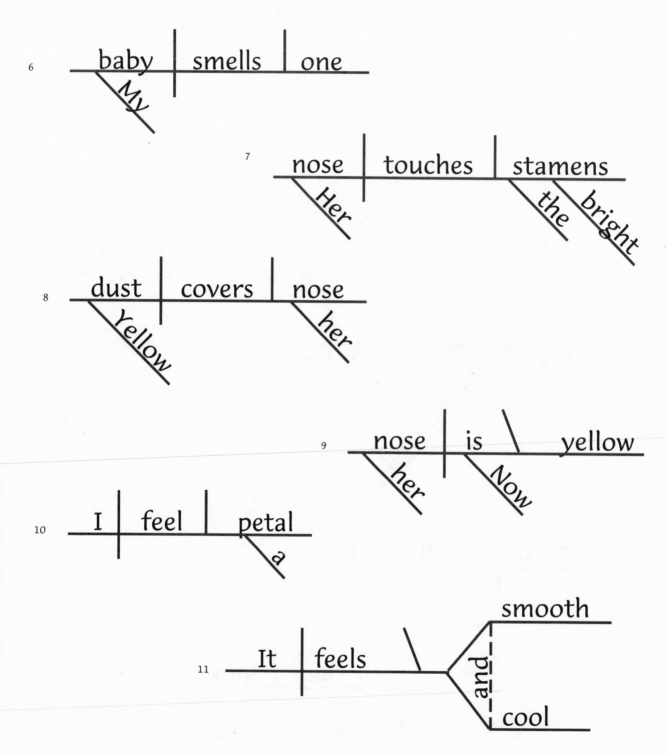

Continued -- for page 46

¹²One blossom is droopy. ¹³Its single task is completed.
¹⁴Our task of worship remains.

¹⁵How gracious is the Lord! ¹⁶Let his house be ever beautiful!

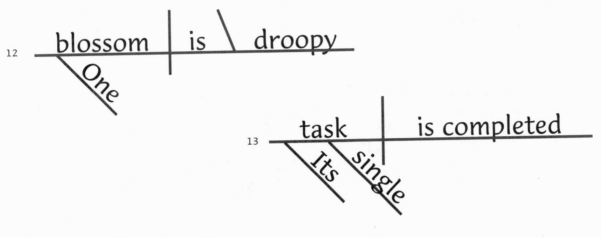

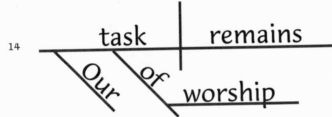

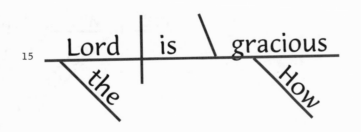

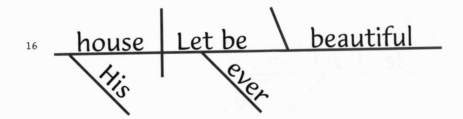

Identifying adverbs for page 48

[1]Jack comes back very quickly. [2]He will certainly come again tomorrow. [3]He will not wait long. [4]He will climb the huge beanstalk very quietly. [5]He will climb down much faster. [6]His axe will be very sharp then. [7]Mother will cut the magic beanstalk immdiately.

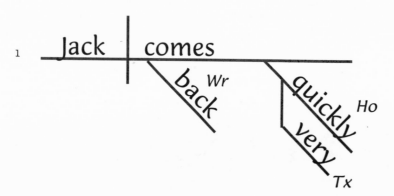

How? Ho
Why? Wy
When? Wn
Where? Wr
To what extent? Tx

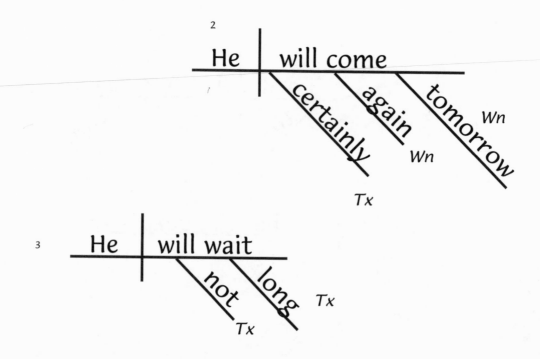

4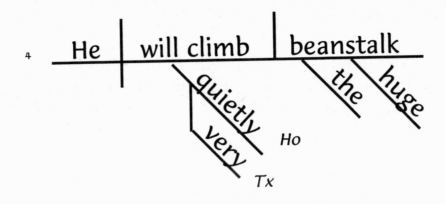

5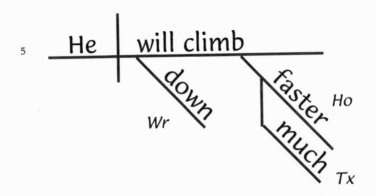

6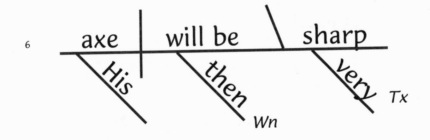

7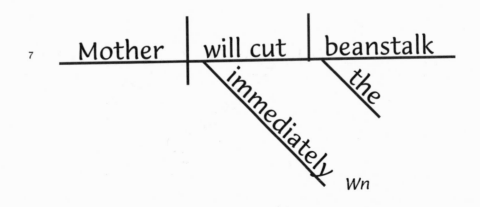

Diagrams for page 50

[1]America really needed some speedy help. [2]Old Ben Franklin bravely crossed the wide ocean. [3]He spoke urgently to the French. [4]Eventually, he returned happily. [5]French help would decisively assist our Revolution.

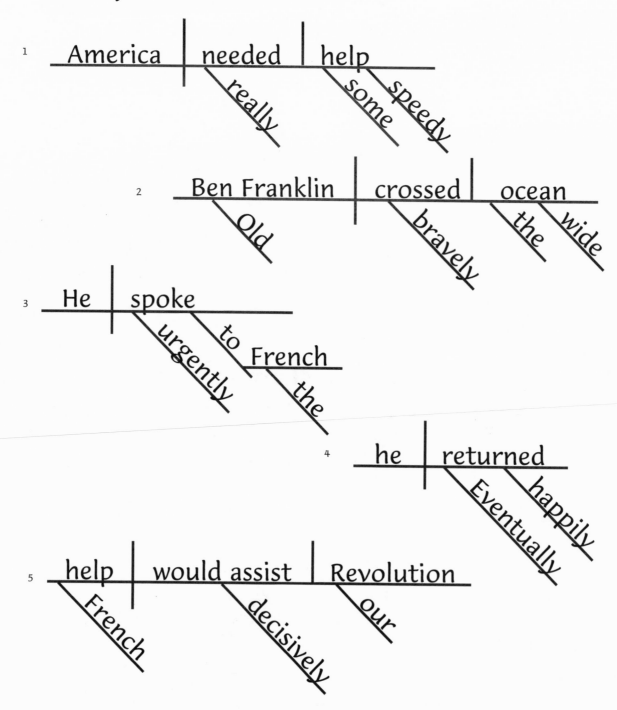

Diagrams for page 51

[1]The good carpenter measures carefully. [2]He measures twice. [3]He marks his cut exactly. [4]Then his sharp saw whistles through. [5]It cuts very quickly. [6]The cut runs perfectly true.

[7]The careless carpenter measures once; then he cuts twice. [8]His first cut always runs askew. [9]Consequently, he must cut again. [10]Carpenters always say, "measure once, cut twice; measure twice, cut once."

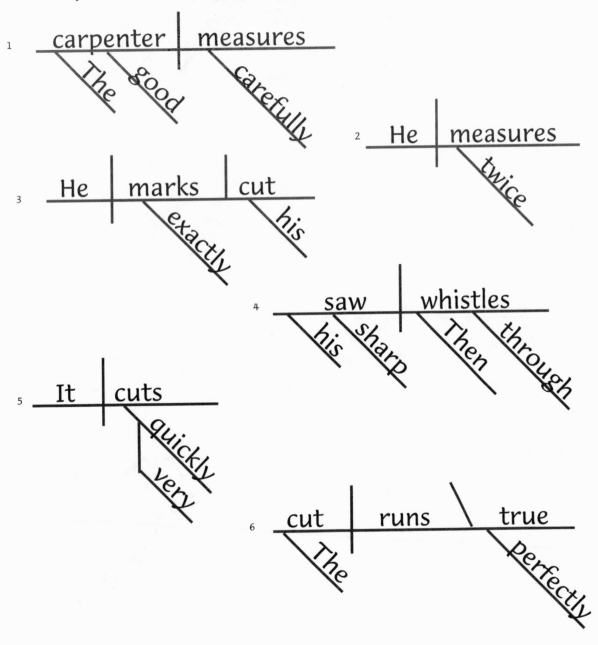

Diagrams for page 52

[7]The careless carpenter measures once; then he cuts twice.
[8]His first cut always runs askew. [9]Consequently, he must cut
again. [10]Carpenters always say, "measure once, cut twice; measure twice, cut once.

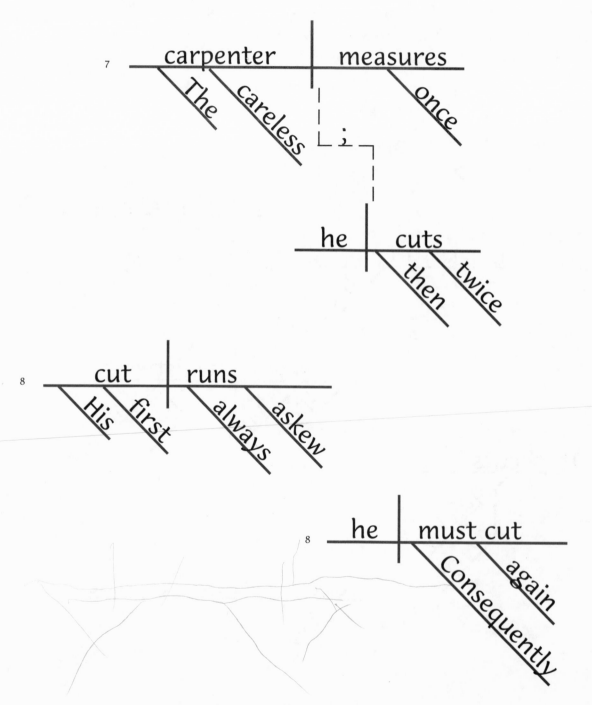

Diagram for page 53

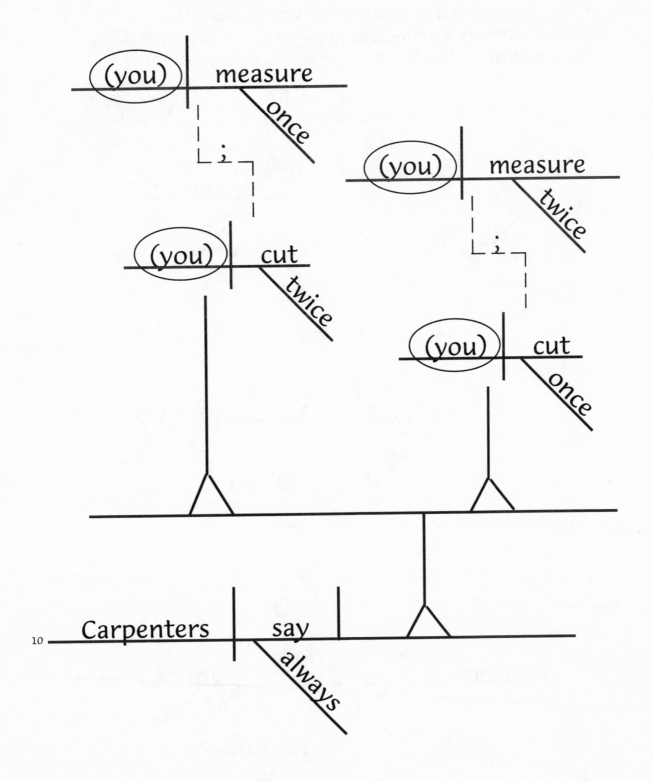

Diagrams for page 56-57

[1]The day before my graduation was so hectic!
[2]We went away during the summer.
[3]America after the Revolution was a new country.

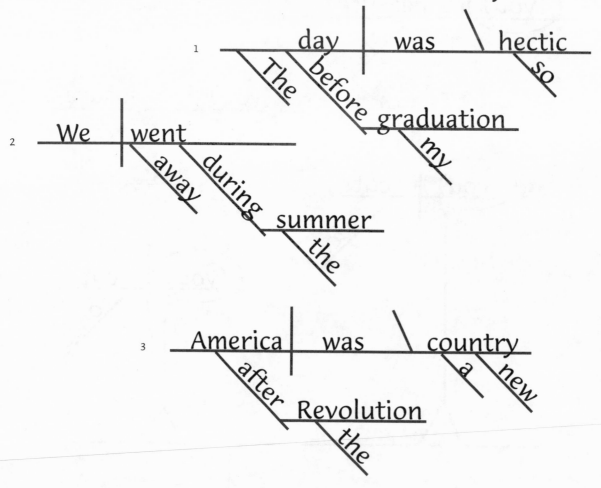

But if you say: *After the Revolution, America was a new country, then you have an adverbial phrase:*

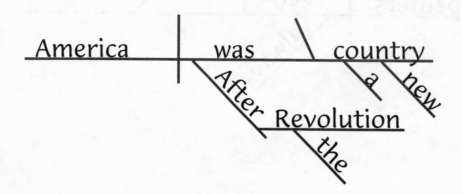

Diagrams for page 57

She went into the house.
They looked eagerly towards the mountain.
Take this for your health.

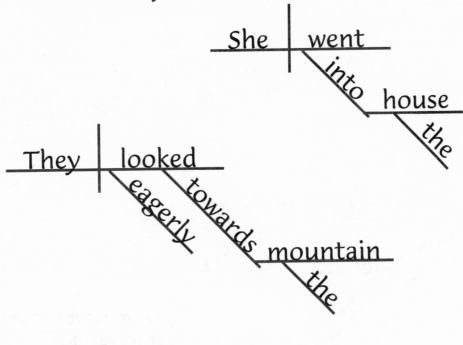

Diagrams for page 59

[1]The book is on the table.
[2]The book on the table is very interesting.
[3]The book is written in French.
[4]The book in French is funny.

Where is the book?

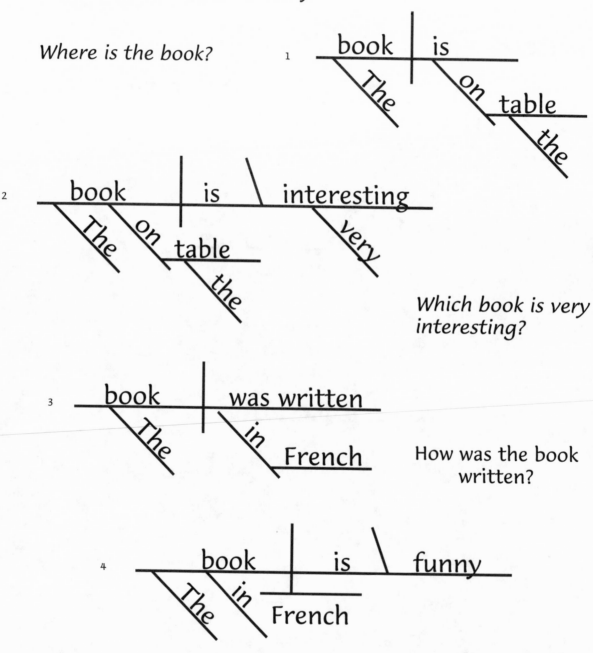

Which book is very interesting?

How was the book written?

Which book is funny?

Diagrams for page 60

⁵The month before your visit went slowly.
⁶I finished my work before your visit.
⁷After a storm, we appreciate the gentle rainbow.
⁸The sky after a storm fills with golden light.

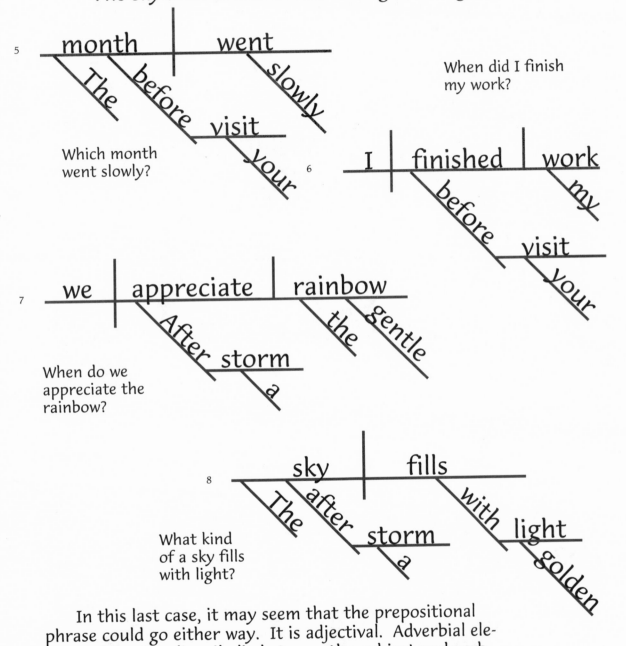

5

Which month
went slowly?

When did I finish
my work?

6

7

When do we
appreciate the
rainbow?

8

What kind
of a sky fills
with light?

In this last case, it may seem that the prepositional phrase could go either way. It is adjectival. Adverbial elements do not ordinarily lie between the subject and verb. It is considered poor construction -- precisely because of this ambiguity. The poet and the breathless child may be excused, however.

Diagrams for page 61

[1]America grew quickly after the revolution. [2]The colonies along the Atlantic spread from that coastline, past the mountains, across the plains, and towards the western ocean. [3]People of various nations came across the sea to the new country for many reasons.

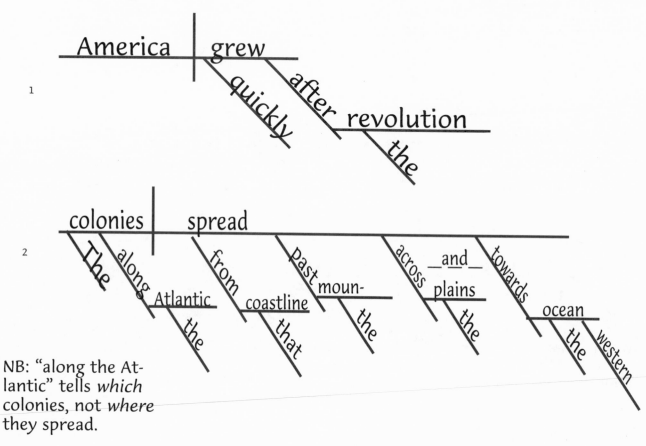

NB: "along the Atlantic" tells *which* colonies, not *where* they spread.

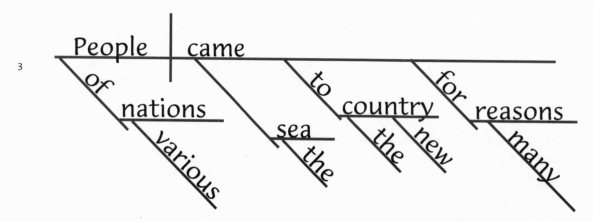

Diagrams for page 62

[4]Some came for the hope of religious freedom. [5]Some sought prosperity in the new land. [6]Some of the most adventurous seemed merely the restless children of a smaller continent. [7]Many of them would build homes for their families, in an unsettled wilderness, amidst political turmoil.

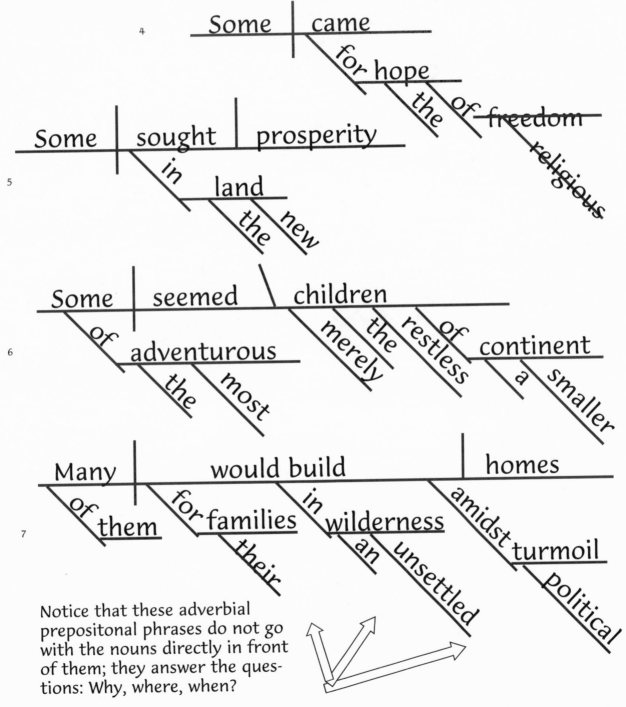

Notice that these adverbial prepositonal phrases do not go with the nouns directly in front of them; they answer the questions: Why, where, when?

Diagram for page 66

Our sweet new teacher chuckled merrily when her bright red apple arrived in a big bucket.

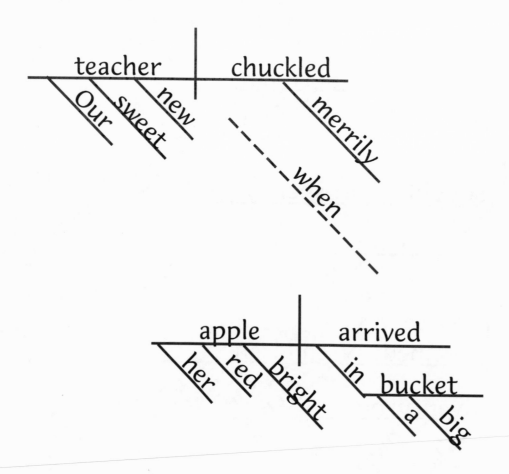

Diagram for page 67

When the nuts ripened amidst the high dense foliage, the young squirrels chased each other merrily through the branches of the tall walnut tree.

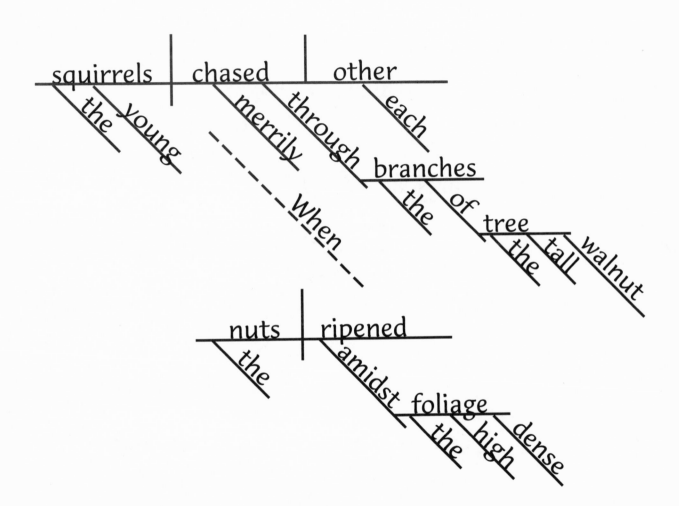

Diagram for page 68

Leaves which are composed of several leaflets are called compound leaves.

Leaves which have paired leaflets are pinnately compound.

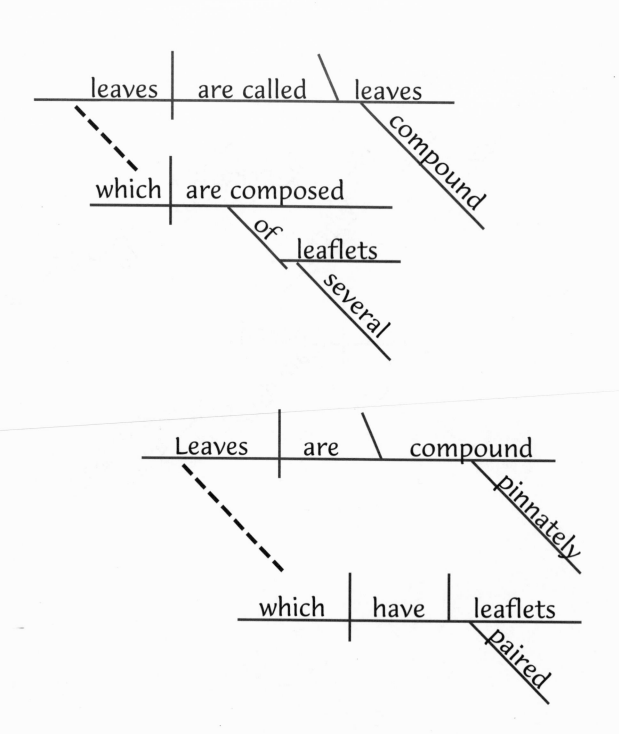

Diagram for page 69

That leaves can be doubly pinnate is truly wondrous.

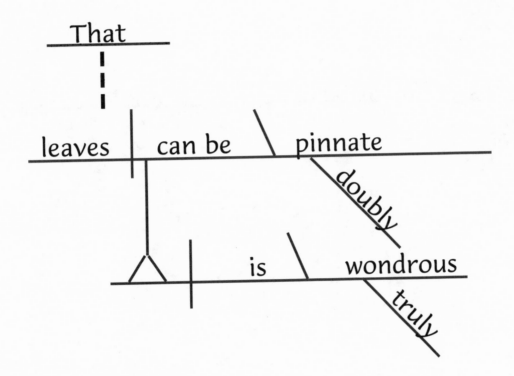

Diagram for page 69 -70

That many ferns must be called triply pinnate is now clear, for they have doubly pinnately compound leaflets.

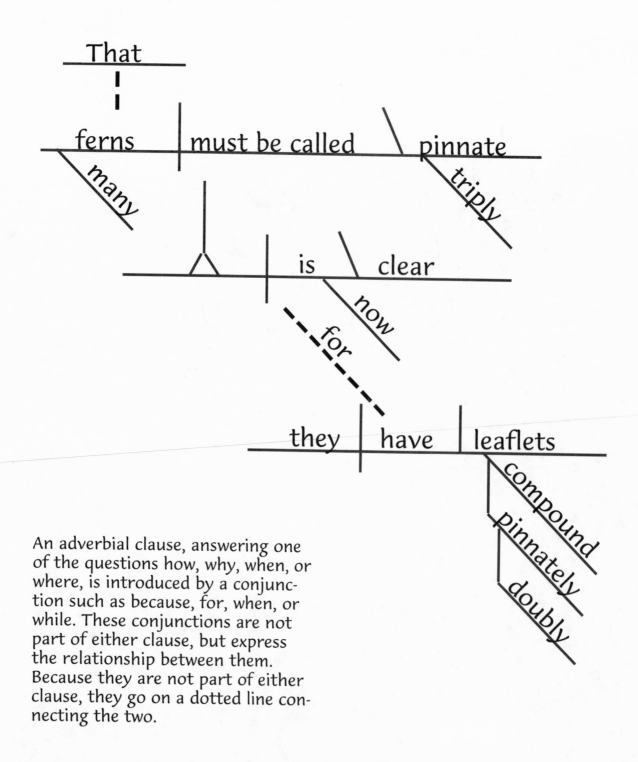

An adverbial clause, answering one of the questions how, why, when, or where, is introduced by a conjunction such as because, for, when, or while. These conjunctions are not part of either clause, but express the relationship between them. Because they are not part of either clause, they go on a dotted line connecting the two.

Diagram for page 70-71

   Leaves, which provide necessary oxygen for us, show that important works may be done humbly, for they are wholly commonplace.

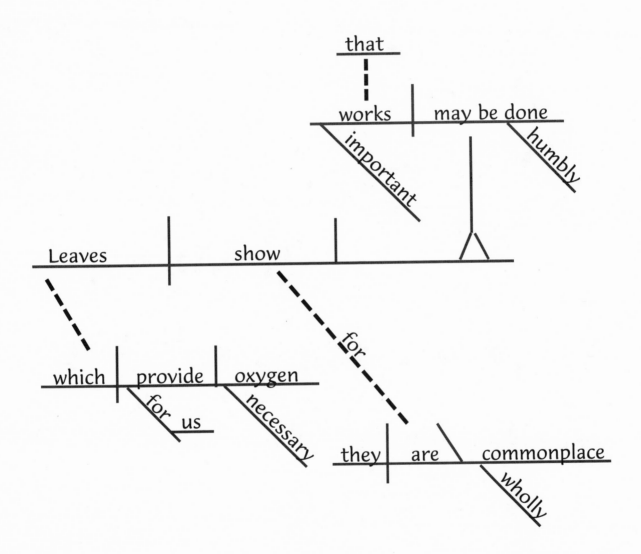

Elementary
Diagramming
Worktext

Mary O. Daly

© Mary O. Daly
ISBN # 09978-0-9825521-0-0

www.hedgeschool.com

Ye Hedge School
24934 478 Ave
Garretson SD. 57030

First edition: August, 1998
Second edition: September, 2002
Third edition: September, 2006
Fourth edition: October, 2009